Patterns of Living

FOUNDATIONS OF SCIENCE LIBRARY

The Natural World
(4 volumes)

The Majesty of the Heavens
(*Foundations of Astronomy*)

The Round World
(*Foundations of Geology and Geomorphology*)

The Skies and the Seas
(*Foundations of Meteorology, Oceanography & Cartography*)

The Ages of the Earth
(*Foundations of Palaeogeography and Palaeontology*)

The Biological Sciences
(6 volumes)

The Life of Animals without Backbones
(*Foundations of Invertebrate Zoology*)

The Life of Animals with Backbones
(*Foundations of Vertebrate Zoology*)

The World of Plants
(*Foundations of Botany*)

Breeding and Growing
(*Foundations of Genetics, Anthropology and Agriculture*)

Patterns of Living
(*Foundations of Ecology*)

Human Kind
(*Foundations of Human Biology*)

The Physical Sciences
(9 volumes)

The Restlessness of Matter
(*Foundations of Aerodynamics, Hydrodynamics and Thermodynamics*)

The Science of Movement
(*Foundations of Mechanics and Sound*)

Lightning in Harness
(*Foundations of Electricity*)

The Silent Energy
(*Foundations of Electrical Technology*)

The Cathode Ray Revolution
(*Foundations of Electronics*)

The Rays of Light
(*Foundations of Optics*)

The Unseen Spectrum
(*Foundations of Electromagnetic Radiation*)

The Cosmic Power
(*Foundations of Nuclear Physics*)

The Discipline of Numbers
(*Foundations of Mathematics*)

The Chemical Sciences
(4 volumes)

The Fundamental Materials
(*Foundations of Basic Chemistry*)

The Elements and their Order
(*Foundations of Inorganic Chemistry*)

The Giant Molecules
(*Foundations of Organic Chemistry*)

The Chemist at Work
(*Foundations of Analysis and Laboratory Techniques*)

Technology
(5 volumes)

The Metallic Skills
(*Foundations of Metallurgy*)

Industrial Processing
(*Foundations of Industrial and Chemical Technology*)

Engineering Technology
(*Foundations of Applied Engineering*)

Automobile Engineering
(*Foundations of Car Mechanics*)

The Inventive Genius
(*Foundations of Scientific Inventions*)

History and Reference
(3 volumes)

The Beginnings of Science
(*Foundations of Scientific History*)

Frontiers of Science
(*Foundations of Research Methods*)

A Dictionary of Scientific Terms
(*The Foundations of Science Reference Book*)

Patterns of Living

Foundations of Ecology

MICHAEL CHINERY, B.A. DAVID LARKIN, B.Sc.

FOUNDATIONS OF SCIENCE LIBRARY

THE BIOLOGICAL SCIENCES

DISTRIBUTED IN THE U.S.A. BY
Ginn and Company: *BOSTON*
PUBLISHED BY
Sampson Low, Marston and Co: *LONDON*

This new presentation assembles
freshly edited material from
'Understanding Science' on one
subject into a single volume.

Library of Congress Catalog Card
Number: 66–18000

Catalog No.: L–20755

Made and printed in Great Britain by
Purnell & Sons Ltd., Paulton
(Somerset) and London

ECOLOGY

Contents

The Living Organism

The Living Organism

BIOLOGY is the study of animals and plants – the study of living things. The word is derived from the Greek *bios* meaning 'life'. One must, therefore, distinguish between living and non-living matter. What, for example, is the difference between the soil and the rocks on the one hand, and the animals and plants among them, on the other? In this case the difference is fairly obvious but what about dead plants and animals? They consist of similar materials to those found in living organisms, yet they have no life.

We cannot answer the question 'What is life?', yet, by studying those features that are common to all living things, and are absent from inanimate objects, we can distinguish between living and non-living things. These features are the visible results of what we call 'life'.

The first, and perhaps the most obvious feature of living things is

The plant in the open grows up straight in response to the light but the one indoors by the window bends over towards the light.

movement. The ability to move from place to place, under their own power, is not possessed by inanimate objects. Movement in animals is quite obvious; perhaps to search for food, or to escape from enemies. Plants can also move, however, as can be shown by placing a pot-plant on the windowsill. The shoot bends over towards the light. Many tiny plants live in water and, apart from the green colouring matter (chlorophyll) are just like tiny animals, swimming about by means

The flat-worm is very sensitive to chemicals in the water and moves towards a food source and away from acid by an almost reflex action. It thus remains in the most favourable places.

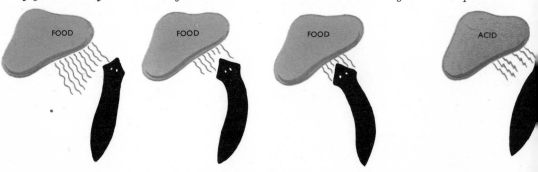

of whiplike hairs (flagella).

Allied to movement is the feature of *irritability*. This means that the organism reacts in a certain way to its surroundings. For example, a flatworm will move away if it senses acid in the water.

The plant described above is reacting to the light. There are other, less obvious examples of sensitivity, e.g. the mouth-watering effect produced by salivary glands when stimulated by the presence of food.

Plants absorb carbon dioxide and water from their surroundings and, by the process of photosynthesis, build up sugars. These, together with mineral salts, go to build up proteins and new parts of the plant. Animals eat plants directly or else they eat other animals, but ultimately the animals all depend upon plants for their food materials. This process of absorbing material and using it to build up new substances is called *nutrition*.

Closely connected with nutrition is the phenomenon of *growth*. Increase in size is not confined to living matter. Crystals grow, but the mechanism is very different from that in living organisms. Whereas in the latter, material is taken in, broken down and

Movement is a characteristic of the living organism.

reconstituted, and then used throughout the body, in crystals more of the same material is added at the surface only. All living things need energy in order to remain alive and distinct from their surroundings. The process that releases the energy is called *respiration*. Sugar is oxidised in both plants and animals and the process may be represented by the equation:

$$C_6H_{12}O_6 + 6O_2 \rightleftharpoons 6CO_2 + 6H_2O + energy$$

glucose (sugar) + oxygen → carbon dioxide + water

This very simplified equation shows the net result but does not show any of the many intermediate stages. Many bacteria can exist without free oxygen; energy is obtained from other chemical reactions.

As a result of respiration, a large amount of carbon dioxide is produced. This must be removed. In vertebrate animals it normally passes out through the lungs or gills, using the same route

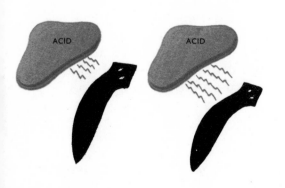

To show that living things respire, air is drawn through the apparatus from left to right. The soda-lime absorbs carbon dioxide but the limewater on the right turns cloudy showing that the animal is respiring. This experiment also works with seeds.

as the oxygen breathed in. In other animals it normally passes out through the skin. During the building up of new body materials there are complicated chemical reactions involving nitrogen-containing compounds Some of the latter are waste products and must also be disposed of. In animals, this is the work of the kidney or other *excretory* organs. The processes of getting rid of waste (both carbon dioxide and nitrogenous compounds) is called *excretion*.

Whereas a stone or a piece of iron can exist almost indefinitely, a living organism can have only a limited life. The cells and protoplasm of which living things are made cannot go on growing indefinitely. Most of them periodically divide into two new cells. In simple, single-celled organisms such as *Amoeba* or *Euglena*, this process results in two new organisms but in higher animals and plants this cannot be. The process of *reproduction* is more complicated. Small regions, or even single cells are cut off from the main body and these begin to grow into completely new individuals, each of which can grow and reach a maximum size and then reproduce again.

These features outlined above are all expressions of life but do not answer the question 'what is life?' There is, as yet, no satisfactory answer to this question. It may be that life is a property of a certain combination of chemical compounds – in which case it may be possible to produce life artificially, or else life may be something extra to the material of the organism.

There has been a great deal of discussion and argument about the origins of life. It is unlikely that this question will ever be completely answered but, obviously, life did begin somewhere at sometime, and since then living things have spread over the whole of the Earth's surface, from the sea-bed to the tops of the mountains. Life in some of these habitats is described on the following pages.

Life in the Sea

The Marine Environment

ABOUT two-thirds of the surface of the Earth is covered by the sea. This means there are something like one hundred and forty million square miles of sea-surface. The average depth has been calculated at about twelve and a half thousand feet or over two miles, making a vast volume of water available as a home for fishes and other animals. In reality the oceans contain a number of different habitats, each with its own collection of animals; habitats such as the seashore, the high seas, and the ocean

substances by photosynthesis. This process requires sunlight—another factor to be considered in the economy of the sea. The depth to which light penetrates depends upon the amount of sediment in the water, but in the open ocean, dim light can be recorded down to a depth of about two thousand feet. Below this, there is the total darkness of the 'deep sea'. Plants are restricted to the upper few hundred feet where there is enough light for photosynthesis. Seaweeds grow on the floor of the

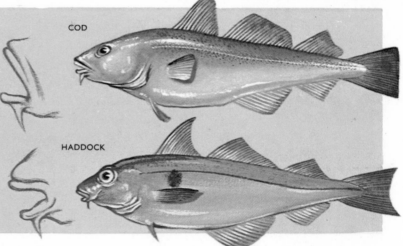

Although the Cod and Haddock live in the same areas, the former feeds on herring and the other fish, while the Haddock lives on bottom-living animals. The position of the mouth in these fish reflects this difference. That of the Haddock is placed lower down.

COD

HADDOCK

floor. Surrounding most of the land masses there is a submerged platform —the *continental shelf*—which slopes down to a depth of about six hundred feet. Beyond this is a steeper region— the *continental slope*—which falls away to the depths of the ocean. Conditions in these three regions differ considerably.

All life in the sea—as on land— depends upon plants and their ability to manufacture food from inorganic

continental shelf, extending sometimes to a depth of about 100 feet. Coastal waters are normally too cloudy to allow enough light to penetrate further. These seaweeds usually play only a small role compared with that of the floating microscopic plants of the *plankton*. The surface layers of the seas support a vast population of these tiny plants, which provide food for a host of

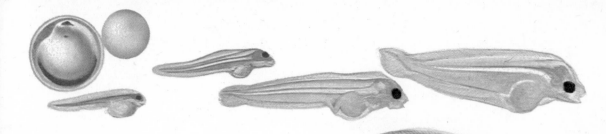

microscopic animals—young fish, crustaceans and molluscs, together with protozoans and jellyfish. This animal plankton is eaten by the larger animals that complete the food chains in the sea. As these animals die, their remains fall to the bottom where they provide abundant food for the bottom-living animals—the *benthos*. The latter—worms, molluscs, sea-urchins, etc.—form the diet of many bottom-feeding fish. The number of bottom-living animals normally falls as the sea gets deeper—for there is less food material falling from above; dead organisms are eaten or decomposed before they reach the bottom.

Animals characteristic of the deep seas begin to appear at about fifteen hundred feet down. They include strange fishes, squids and many types of crustaceans—shrimps, prawns, etc. Many of them have light-producing organs to aid them in the deep, dark waters. The fishes are frequently fiercely carnivorous; many of them have huge mouths and have been described as 'floating fish-traps'. Interesting as these deep-sea animals are, they are commercially unimportant. The majority of fishes exist in shallows and the upper layers of the seas where there is plenty of food.

The distribution of fish depends ultimately upon the distribution of the plankton. In tropical regions the warm surface waters do not mix with the colder, deeper water. This means that the material which sinks to the bottom is not replaced. These

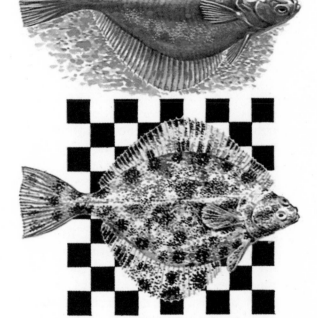

The Plaice starts life as a normally shaped fish, but owing to uneven growth of the skull both eyes come to be on the right side. The fish then lies on its left side. It can change its colour to match the background.

regions do not support such enormous numbers of plankton—and therefore fish—as the cooler temperate regions. The food material released from the decaying organisms falling to the bottom is caught up in the deep ocean currents. When these currents

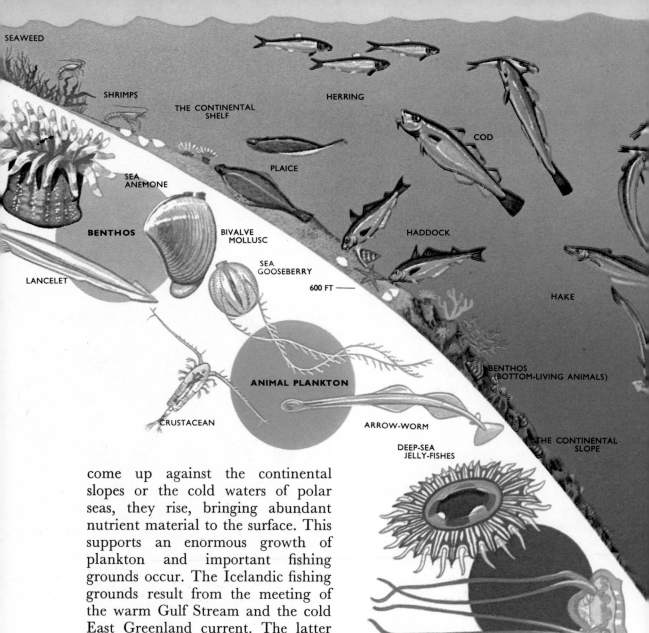

SEAWEED

SHRIMPS

THE CONTINENTAL SHELF

HERRING

COD

PLAICE

SEA ANEMONE

BENTHOS

BIVALVE MOLLUSC

HADDOCK

LANCELET

SEA GOOSEBERRY

600 FT ——

HAKE

ANIMAL PLANKTON

BENTHOS (BOTTOM-LIVING ANIMALS)

CRUSTACEAN

ARROW-WORM

THE CONTINENTAL SLOPE

DEEP-SEA JELLY-FISHES

come up against the continental slopes or the cold waters of polar seas, they rise, bringing abundant nutrient material to the surface. This supports an enormous growth of plankton and important fishing grounds occur. The Icelandic fishing grounds result from the meeting of the warm Gulf Stream and the cold East Greenland current. The latter sinks because it is denser and forces up the rich waters of the Gulf Stream. In shallow regions such as the North Sea there is continued mixing of the waters and plenty of river-borne material. Abundant plankton and benthos make the North Sea a valuable fishing ground.

The Herring is an important pelagic fish. Cod is certainly the most important *demersal* fish of Northern waters. Demersal is a term used to cover those fish living on or near the bottom of the sea, as opposed to

The various regions of the sea, with their different conditions, support very different populations of animals. Plants are found only in the upper layers where there is light.

the *pelagic* fish such as Herring and Tunny which swim in the upper layers of open water. A full-grown female Cod may lay more than two million eggs in a season. The eggs float in the plankton and large numbers of them and the young fishes

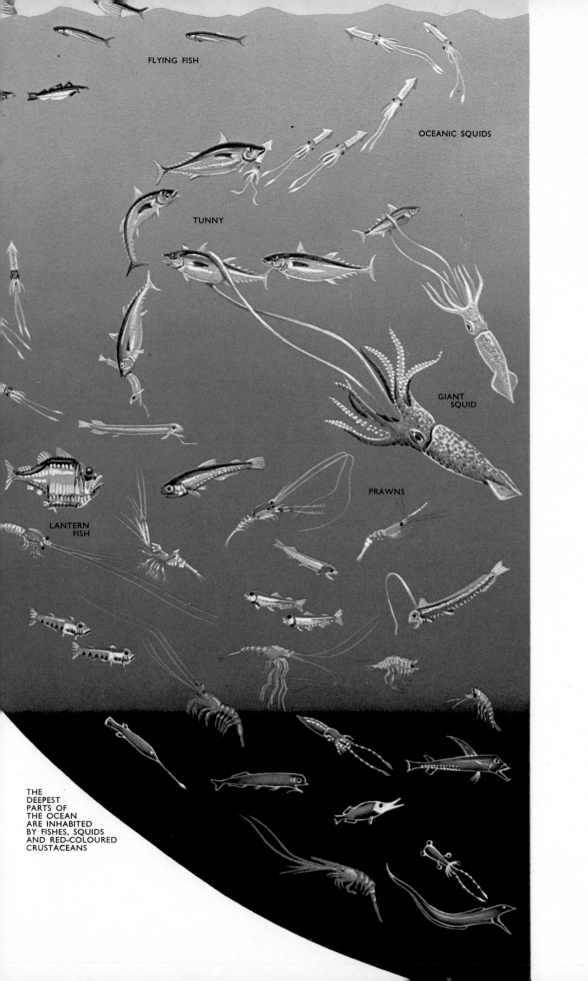

FLYING FISH

OCEANIC SQUIDS

TUNNY

GIANT
SQUID

PRAWNS

LANTERN
FISH

THE
DEEPEST
PARTS OF
THE OCEAN
ARE INHABITED
BY FISHES, SQUIDS
AND RED-COLOURED
CRUSTACEANS

are eaten. The young fishes feed upon the planktonic plants and animals for two to three months and then (when about an inch long) they swim to the bottom. Here they feed on small crustaceans and other bottom-living animals and reach maturity in about five years. By this time the Cod are about two feet long. The adults feed mainly on Herring and other fish.

Some interesting demersal types are the flat-fish – Plaice, Flounder, Sole and Turbot, to name only a few. These fishes are flattened from side to side and they lie on one side on the sea-bed. The first three all lie on their left side, whereas the Turbot lies on its right.

The Plaice lays floating eggs. The young begin life as normally shaped fish, feeding on the plankton for a few weeks. After about a month the skull begins to grow unevenly, with the result that the left eye is pushed over on to the right side. By now, the

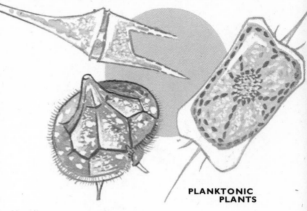

PLANKTONIC PLANTS

Tiny floating plants such as these are the first members of the sea's food chain.

fish, seven or eight weeks old, has descended to the sea-bed where it rests on its left side. The upper (right) side is coloured and can be altered to match the background, whether it be sand, gravel or some artificial background. The Plaice becomes mature in four or five years, or even earlier if food is particularly abundant. The adults feed upon worms and molluscs.

SOME DEEP-SEA FISHES

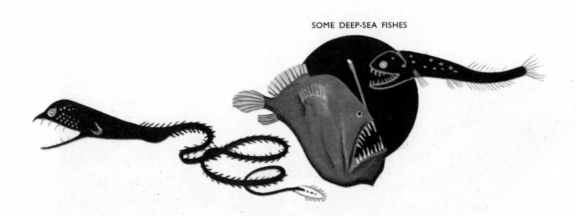

CHAPTER THREE

The Pastures of the Sea – The Floating Plankton

PARTICULARLY important in the economy of the sea are the myriads of floating and drifting creatures and plants found mainly in the surface waters. These plants and animals are collectively called *plankton*. The majority are microscopic and are suspended in the water in much the same quantities as the dust particles we sometimes see in a beam of light.

Not enough light penetrates below 150 feet in most parts of the sea to are sometimes called 'the pastures of the sea'.

The tiny animals of the plankton (mainly crustaceans called copepods) graze on the plants. They are preyed on by larger animals (e.g., herring) which in turn are eaten by larger fish (e.g., cod)—a series which is called a *food chain*. In the sea there are many such food chains, some of them ending in ourselves when we eat fish.

The pastures of the sea are incred-

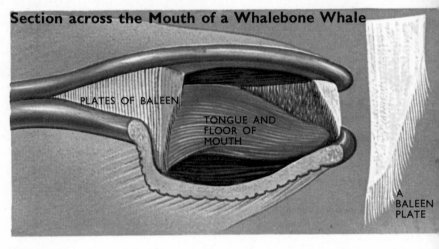

Section across the Mouth of a Whalebone Whale

PLATES OF BALEEN

TONGUE AND FLOOR OF MOUTH

A BALEEN PLATE

The whalebone whales have fringed plates of baleen hanging from their gums. The mouth is filled with water, and, as it closes, its floor and tongue are raised so forcing water out through the plates which sieve off the tiny shrimp-like creatures.

enable the plants to produce their own food so they occur only in the upper layers. Only green plants are able to manufacture their own food from carbon dioxide and water, using the energy of sunlight. All animals therefore depend on plants for their food, for if they themselves do not eat plants they eat other animals that have eaten plants.

The planktonic plants are responsible for making nearly all the food material in the sea. This is why they ibly rich, more luxuriant than any on land. An area of sea may produce a greater quantity of plants than the same area of tropical forest. From 1953 to 1955 the average annual catch of fish was nearly 27,000,000 tons. This is mainly made up of about a dozen kinds of fish (e.g., herring, cod, haddock). There are over 20,000 kinds of fish altogether and the fish actually caught are but a proportion of the fish of each kind. It has been estimated that a thousand tons of

Under a microscope the planktonic plants and animals show an endless variety of forms.

Key to Illustration

1. *Ceratium tripos* (dinoflagellate). 2. *Asterionella* (diatom). 3. *Grammatophora* (diatom). 4. *Euchaeta* (copepod). 5. *Rhizosolenia* (diatom). 6. *Ditylium* (diatom). 7. *Palinurus* larva (a lobster, crustacean). 8. *Pleurobrachia* (comb jelly). 9. *Peridinium granii* (dinoflagellate). 10. *Clio* (sea snail). 11. Brittle Star larva, an ophiopluteus. 12. *Aulacantha* (protozoan). 13. Arrow-worm. 14. *Cypridina* (crustacean). 15. *Biddulphia* (diatom). 16. *Peridinium depressum* (dinoflagellate). 17. *Eucampia* (diatom). 18. *Phaeodactylum* (formerly *Nitzschia*) (diatom). 19. *Chaetoceros* (diatom). 20. *Ceratium furca* (dinoflagellate). 21. Copepod larva, a *nauplius*. 22. *Rissoa* larva (sea snail). 23. *Calanus finmarchicus* (copepod). 24. *Turritopsis* (Jellyfish). 25. *Globigerina* (protozoan). 26. *Meganyctiphanes norvegica* (shrimp-like crustacean). 27. *Balanus* larva, a nauplius (a barnacle, crustacean). 28. A group of *Noctiluca* (dinoflagellates).

plants will result in one ton of fish. From these figures some idea is obtained of the immense richness of the sea's pastures.

The plants of the plankton are called phytoplankton, the animals are called zooplankton. The phytoplankton is made up of several different

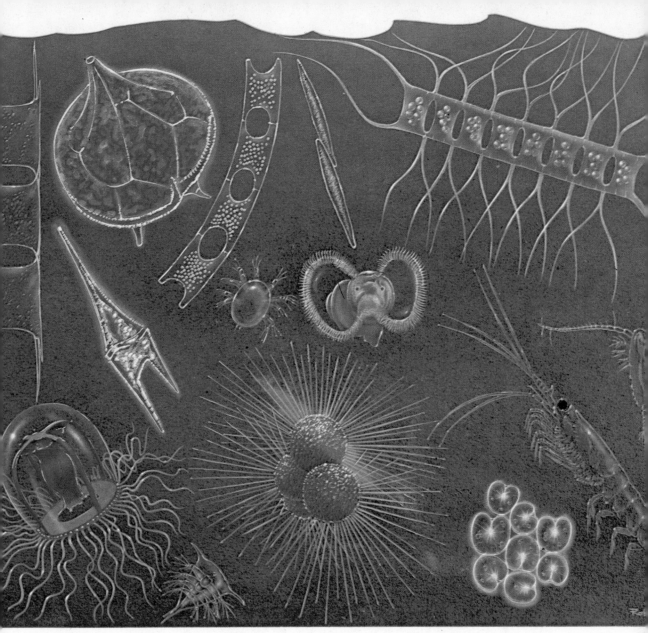

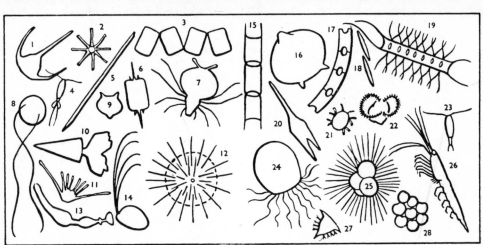

A green plant's food making process is called photosynthesis. The energy needed to drive it is the energy of sunlight. It can only take place therefore in the sunlit upper layers of the oceans. On a very bright day (*left*) the region where photosynthesis is greatest is just below the surface because the light at the surface is *too* bright and slows photosynthesis down. On a dull day, however, most photosynthesis will take place at the surface.

Many of the animals in the plankton rise towards the surface each night (*left*) and sink or swim actively downwards in the daytime (*right*). Probably they prefer to live in water which is getting a particular amount of light. As the sun sets its rays do not penetrate far into the water because they enter almost horizontally. The animals seek the amount of light they want by swimming up to the surface. The next dawn finds them still near the surface and as the sun climbs its rays strike deeper into the water. The animals move downwards so that they stay in water receiving the amount of light they prefer.

kinds of plants (though they all come from one plant group, the algae) including diatoms, dinoflagellates, silicoflagellates, coccolithophores and the nannoplankton.

Diatoms usually form the bulk of the phytoplankton. They are single-celled and each is an irregular sac of protoplasm (living jelly) surrounded by a delicate, transparent box or shell. The shell is in two halves which are arranged one inside the other like the lid and base of a shoe polish tin. It is made of a glass-like substance, silica, and is often beautifully sculptured, even drawn into spines, forming incredible shapes. Pigments give diatoms a brown-green or yellow colour. They range in size from $\frac{1}{2500}$ inch to $\frac{1}{250}$ inch.

Dinoflagellates have two small

The Economy of the Sea

The tiny green plants in the surface layers of the sea are continually using up the chemicals dissolved in the sea water in their food making processes. They are eaten by tiny animals which are eaten by larger animals. More tiny plants grow in place of the eaten plants and, in growing, they use up more chemicals. And so the process goes on. How is it, then, that the chemicals are not used up completely?

The main materials that a green plant needs are carbon dioxide and water. From these, using the energy of sunlight, it is able to make sugars and starch. Carbon dioxide is present in the air and continually passes from it into the water in which it dissolves.

Besides carbon dioxide and water the plants need minute amounts of mineral salts and other more complicated chemicals. These are constantly being carried to the sea through sewers and in rivers. The Mississippi river alone carries more than 500,000,000 tons of material to the sea each year. Along with the waste products of the sea creatures and their dead or dying bodies all this material sinks slowly to the sea floor. There much of it is decomposed by bacteria or eaten by the remarkable variety of bottom-living animals.

The chemical products of decomposition rise to the surface, carried by vertical currents (due to differences in the temperature and saltiness of the sea water at different levels) or, close inshore, by the stirring action of rough weather. At the surface the chemicals are then available to the growing plants.

The animals in the sea breathe oxygen that is dissolved in the water. This dissolved oxygen, like the carbon dioxide, comes from the atmosphere. Oxygen is also produced and given out by the plants.

There are seasons in the sea just as there are seasons on land. The number of plants and animals in the plankton vary considerably at different times of the year. So do the relative numbers of different kinds of them. This is due to changes in the temperature of the water, changes in its salt content (salinity), the amount of light (this varies tremendously from summer to winter), the quantities of food materials available and also breeding seasons. The zooplankton are dependent on the tiny green plants for their food so that variations in the number of plants are followed very closely by variations in the numbers of animals.

whip-like hairs (flagella). By beating these they are able to swim. Their cell walls are made of little plates of cellulose. Some are luminous producing a brilliant light which is especially visible at night.

Silicoflagellates are about $\frac{1}{5000}$ inch long. They were not discovered until recently because they pass through the finest nets. They are covered in tiny plates of silica.

Coccolithophores have tiny plates of chalk and often give the water a milky-white appearance.

The nannoplankton is made up of minute green plants, which are between $\frac{1}{25000}$ inch and $\frac{1}{5000}$ inch long. They pass through the finest silk nets.

The animal plankton is drawn from a large number of groups. It includes protozoans (single-celled animals), jellyfish, worms, snails, arrow worms and, above all, crustaceans, particularly copepods (oar-footed creatures). These all spend their entire life as plankton. Others, such as fishes, starfishes and many molluscs, are only planktonic as eggs or when young.

CHAPTER FOUR

Nekton – The Swimmers

THE animals that swim freely in the sea are collectively called *nekton*. There is no sharp dividing line between nekton and plankton (the floating and drifting life in the surface waters). Many fishes, for instance, are planktonic when young but are able to swim actively against the currents when they are older. Similarly, many fishes spend a great deal of their time on the sea-floor but swim freely when they are searching for food. Seals and the like spend part of their lives in water and part on land.

Nekton consists mainly of fishes and whales though squids and turtles are also included. Of these, the fishes are the most important commercially and they are certainly more numerous both in terms of species and individuals. There are over twenty thousand species of bony fishes alone (about three thousand species of shark-like fishes). The former group includes the Herring, Mackerel, Plaice, Cod and Haddock – all fishes of commercial importance. It is estimated that the Herring population of the North Atlantic alone must be at least one million million. Many other species accumulate in vast shoals each of which may contain millions of individuals. These figures give some idea of the richness of the sea's pastures for ultimately every animal in the sea depends on the tiny green plants (phytoplankton) living in the surface waters.

Many fishes feed directly on the zooplankton – Herring, Sprat and Mackerel for example. The whalebone whales and the Basking shark also eat animal plankton.

The distribution of plankton changes quite remarkably – partly due to ocean currents but largely because rapid bursts of growth when conditions are good may be followed by a rapid grazing down by the

BLUE SHARK

ALBACORE

OPAH

OARFISH

PILCHARD SPRAT

TUNNY

GLOBEFISH

SAILFISH

SUNFISH

EGGS (enlarged)

DEVELOPING FISH

THE LIFE HISTORY OF THE HERRING

20

The Herring

Like Mackerel, Pilchard and Tunny, the Herring spends much of its time near the surface. It is a *pelagic* fish. It consumes plankton and small fish that are themselves plankton feeders. *Demersal* fish are those that spend most or all of their life on the sea-bed. Examples are Cod, Haddock, Plaice and Skate.

The Herring is a typical pelagic fish in that its colouring makes it remarkably well adapted for life in the surface waters. When viewed from above, the shimmering blue-green of its back matches the darkness beneath. From below the whitish silver of its underside is merged with the light background above. No doubt this light underside also lessens the effect of shadows.

Unlike most pelagic fish, the Herring lay eggs that sink. The spawn is deposited in masses over the sea-floor where it covers the stones, shells and even some of the bottom-dwelling animals. Prior to spawning, the Herring congregate in vast shoals, some of which are said to cover an area of ten square miles or more – such a shoal might contain several hundred million fish. Each female herring lays upwards of ten thousand eggs. Some idea of the amount of spawn produced can be gained from these figures.

Many of the eggs are consumed by bottom-living fish such as Haddock and no doubt other creatures considerably reduce the numbers.

Newly hatched herrings are only a quarter of an inch long. For a few days, each is nourished by a sac of yolk. Once this is used up the young Herring leaves the bottom and reaches the surface where it begins to feed on the phytoplankton. As it grows its diet changes to small zooplankton, particularly the larvae of copepods (oar-footed creatures) and later to adult copepods. The planktonic youngsters are vulnerable to attacks from arrow worms, carnivorous bristle worms and sea gooseberries, and many die.

When it is almost two inches long the young Herring becomes more and more like the adult in shape. Early in life it is somewhat eel-shaped. It also acquires a covering of tiny scales and begins to move into shallow water particularly in estuaries. At this time many are caught and marketed as whitebait together with the sprat, a close relative of the herring. Herring seem to spend approximately six months in coastal waters before they disperse. They only join the large spawning shoals when between three and five years old. This has been discovered by counting the number of rings of growth on the scales.

During the summer the Herring feed voraciously on the rich supply of zooplankton and a wide band is added to the scale during this period; but in the winter when food is scarce nothing is added. Thus each scale has a series of rings of growth and lines, the latter representing no growth in winter. Later in life the growth of the scales slows down and it becomes difficult to read their age accurately. In the summer the Herring build up a reserve of fats and oils. This tides them over the winter until they are able to start feeding again on the spring outburst of plankton.

Fin-whales, Killer whales, porpoises and sea-birds such as seagulls and gannets are among the predators of adult herring. Cod are probably their greatest enemies, however, for the Herring move away from the surface after their nightly feeding excursions. At the bottom many fall victim to cod, as do mackerel. Some captured codfish have had the remains of ten or more herrings in their stomachs. Several of the sharks and rays also feed on herring.

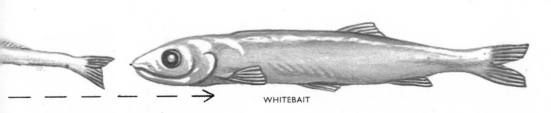

WHITEBAIT

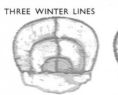

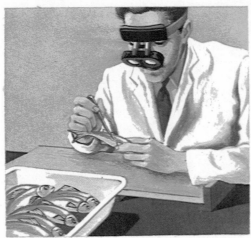

THREE WINTER LINES   FIVE WINTER LINES

(Above) Examining a herring. The age of a herring may be determined by the marking on its scales. Each scale has a series of broad rings, representing summer growth, and lines, representing no growth in winter.

Thresher sharks are said to work together using their enormous tails to drive smaller fish such as mackerel into shoals. These are then consumed.

plankton-feeders and the exhaustion of nitrate and phosphate. This is why the distribution of fish is so patchy. Most of the commercially important fish lay eggs that float (the Herring is an exception). Ocean currents, too, have a direct effect on a fish's distribution. The eggs may be carried to water scarce in plankton. When these hatch, the young fish will have little food and many will die. The absence of a predator's normal food may mean that it consumes an unusually high proportion of young fish. The reverse may also apply. Ocean currents may carry the eggs and young fish to water that is too cold or too warm; it may be too salty or not salty enough. There are many such factors that control the fish population within the sea.

CHAPTER FIVE

Benthos – Life on the Sea Floor

THE sea floor is the least explored part of the Earth's surface. Yet even our present-day knowledge shows that it is a region of great contrasts, stretching from the seashore to the great depths, a region where there are giant mountain ranges, deep chasms and vast plateaux. Just as there are many different types of soils on land, so the sea floor in some places is sandy, in others muddy, gravelly or rocky, and over large areas it is covered with the chalky or sandy shells of tiny animals or with red clay. Only in shallow parts of the sea do the Sun's rays reach it. In slightly deeper parts there is a dim twilight, while below this permanent darkness reigns; a world of silence where conditions hardly vary. A world where the temperature remains at about 3°C. throughout the year and which is disturbed only by the slow-moving deep ocean currents. A world where the enormous pressure, produced by the great weight of water above, would crush any creature not adapted to withstand it. All the forms of life which inhabit the sea floor are collectively called *benthos*. Generally the deeper below the sea surface the sea floor is, the fewer the numbers of living things. The seaweed-infested coastal areas are often richest in animal life, particularly at the edge of the continental shelf (the gently sloping area below the sea shore) at a depth of about 100 fathoms.

The dark, silent and almost unvarying conditions of the deeps may be contrasted with the margins of the sea floor, the seashore, where the animals have very special problems. They are covered and uncovered by the rhythmical comings and goings of high and low tides. At high tide they are immersed in salty water and may be subjected to the full force of the breaking waves. At low tide they may have to contend with a covering of fresh rain-water, or the scorching hot sun of a summer's day.

The sea floor presents a great range of places to live (*habitats*), each presenting its own problems to the animals. The animals of each habitat are beautifully adapted for life there.

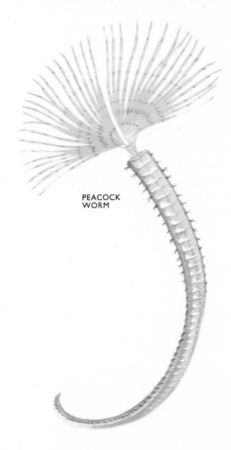

PEACOCK
WORM

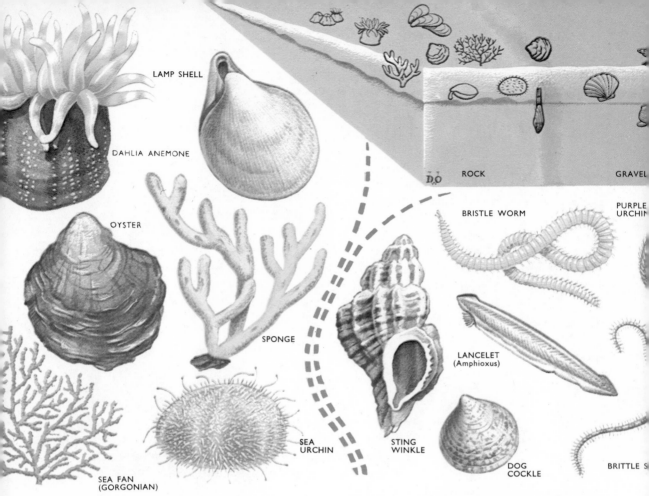

LAMP SHELL

DAHLIA ANEMONE

OYSTER

SPONGE

SEA FAN
(GORGONIAN)

SEA
URCHIN

STING
WINKLE

DOG
COCKLE

ROCK

GRAVEL

BRISTLE WORM

PURPLE
URCHIN

LANCELET
(Amphioxus)

BRITTLE S

A selection of animals from each of the types of bottom shown in the diagram. This shows the distribution of surface-dwelling and burrowing animals. There are many intermediate bottoms between these four types. Gravel may be muddy, and mud and sand are often mixed together.

For example, much of the sea floor is covered with soft, semi-fluid mud, and many of the animals have stalks which hold their bodies up above the mud. This prevents them from sinking into it and from being suffocated. Such are some stalked sea lilies and sponges with long spines sunk into the bottom. One curious fish, the Tripod fish, has three enormously long fins on which it is able to hop about.

Some parts of the sea floor, particularly where the bottom is rocky, may appear like a beautiful underwater "garden" with "forests" of plant-like corals and sponges or patches of flower-like sea anemones. In other parts of the sea floor there appears to be very little life indeed, but below the surface may be found hundreds of burrowing creatures. This is particularly so on sandy or muddy bottoms where a great variety of burrowing worms, molluscs and crabs are found.

On the same deposits in different parts of the ocean very similar animal *communities* will be found, each containing the same groups of animals and usually each community will be dominated by one particular kind of animal whose name it bears. Thus shallow mud is often dominated by the cockle *Cardium* and shallow sand by another bivalve, *Tellina*.

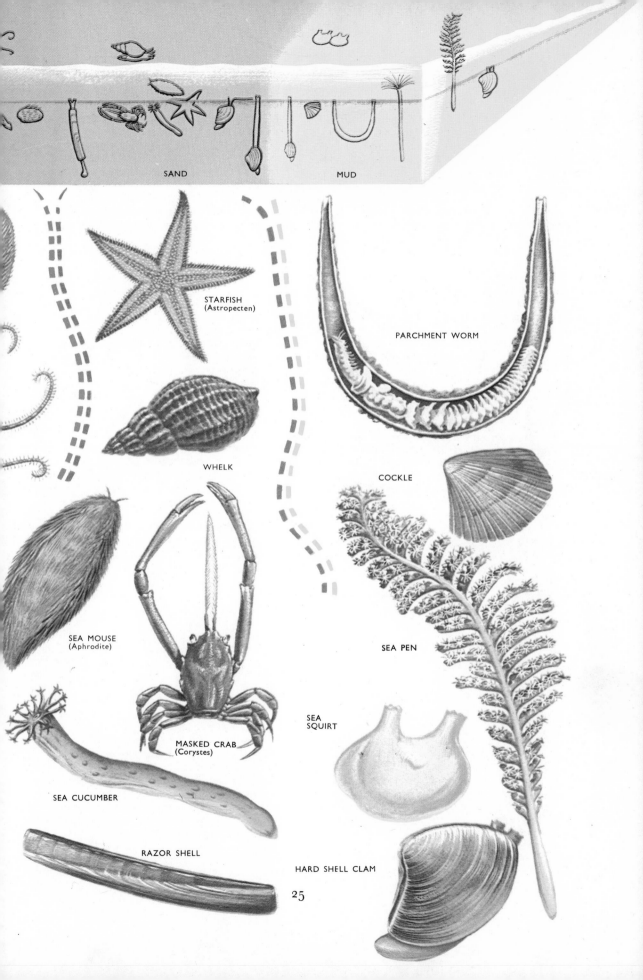

SAND

MUD

STARFISH
(Astropecten)

PARCHMENT WORM

WHELK

COCKLE

SEA MOUSE
(Aphrodite)

SEA PEN

MASKED CRAB
(Corystes)

SEA
SQUIRT

SEA CUCUMBER

RAZOR SHELL

HARD SHELL CLAM

25

Everywhere the surface waters of the oceans teem with minute floating and drifting life, the plankton. As members of the plankton die their remains sink towards the sea floor, falling on it as a continuous rain and forming a thin layer of material. Near the surface many diatoms and single-celled animals (protozoans) live, together with multitudes of bacteria which are breaking down the dead remains. There is thus a rich supply of small food particles for the benthos, the greater part of which (the particle feeders) feeds on it while the larger flesh-eating (carnivorous) creatures, and also many fishes, devour the particle feeders.

The particle feeders are of two main kinds, those that trap the material as it is falling, or in other words eat the suspended particles, (the *suspension feeders*), and those that feed on the fallen material or *detritus* (the *detritus feeders*). These may even consume the sand or mud as well in a similar way to the earthworm eating soil.

On rocky or stony bottoms little detritus can remain for it is removed by the scouring action of waves and currents. Most of the animals will be suspension feeders. Sponges, for example, are like vase-shaped sieves. A water current carrying suspended food particles is drawn in through the walls of the vase, food material is trapped by special cells and the strained water leaves through the opening at the top of the vase. Hydra-like creatures (or hydroids) feed on small animals and plants as well as on dead material. Similarly some sea anemones trap food with their tentacle plumes. Sea fans and some other related types consist of branching colonies. The bulk of each colony is the branched, limestone skeleton, in which the tiny hydra-like polyps are placed at intervals in cup-like depressions. Many hundreds of polyps may be present in one colony, and when they all spread out their tentacles like many upturned umbrellas they can catch considerable quantities of the falling remains of the plankton. Sea pens, relatives of the sea fans, grow in sand or mud, the main part of each colony being held above the sea floor on a stalk.

Many of the bivalve molluscs are suspension feeders. Their breathing organs (gills) act as sieving devices. They are covered with short hair-like structures called cilia, which, in beating, draw a current of water containing food particles in through the opening between the two halves of the shell and pass the food, which is caught up in a sticky slime (mucus), to the mouth.

Mussels (rocky bottom forms), oysters and scallops (gravel and sand) and burrowing forms, such as razor shells, some clams and cockles (found in mud or sand) all feed in this way. Many of these and other bivalves occur in incredible numbers over large areas of the sea bed. All are busy straining the tiny food particles from the water so that each year many tons of food are consumed and much of it is built up into the flesh of the bivalves upon which many of the fishes depend for their food. To a large extent, therefore, the fish population depends on the extraordinary efficiency of the bivalves to "extract" food particles from the water.

Lamp shells, sea squirts, tube-building worms and barnacles and many other crustaceans also feed on suspended food particles. Lamp shells have a two-valved shell. Around the mouth is a coiled crown of tentacles and these are covered by cilia which beat and draw a water current to the mouth.

Many worms build themselves tubes of sand grains, mud shells or even hardened mucus. Some have long, feathery, tentacles which open out like the petals of a flower when the worm projects from its tube. Cilia on the tentacles draw a water current towards the mouth and food and other particles may be guided there in special grooves. The grooves are so arranged that only the small food particles pass to the mouth and larger particles are either rejected or passed to build the tube.

Some of the tube-building worms are also deposit feeders. The water current draws the already settled food particles towards the mouth. Many bristle worms burrow through the sand or mud, eating their way from one place to another and, like earthworms, passing both earth and food through their gut where the food is digested.

Some worms such as *Arenicola*, the lugworm, construct U-shaped burrows.

Sea cucumbers, heart urchins, acorn worms, many bivalves, brittle stars and snail-like molluscs are also detritus feeders. The burrowing bivalves are of great interest. Whereas the shell is kept below the surface the tubes (siphons), carrying a water current over and away from the body, project above the surface. The inhalant siphon is often very long and searches the sea floor like the hose of a miniature vacuum cleaner, drawing in food particles which are passed to the mouth.

The carnivores feed on the detritus and on the suspension feeders. They compete very successfully with the fishes for food. Examples are the starfishes, many kinds of bristle worms, sea anemones, molluscs and crustaceans, including shrimps and prawns.

The sea anemones often trap animals such as shrimps, or even fishes, swimming near their tentacles. Bristle worms such as the

sea mouse, *Aphrodite*, turn their mouths inside out as they shoot them at prey. The prey are gripped with powerful teeth and dragged into the mouth as it is turned in the right way again. Whelks, such as *Buccinum*, are voracious feeders. Like all snail-like molluscs they have a rasp-like tongue or *radula* which is armed with sharp, horny teeth. The radula is flexible, like the blade of a band saw, and is even able to file through the shells of other molluscs.

Most sea slugs feed on hydra-like animals, sea anemones and sometimes sponges. A few feed on seaweeds and are beautifully camouflaged to blend with their surroundings—their body surfaces often being drawn out into seaweed-like outgrowths. These of course are found only in fairly shallow water for the seaweeds on which they feed only grow where they receive enough light for photosynthesis.

Perhaps the main competitors with the fishes for food are the starfishes. The undersides of their arms are covered with rows of hollow tube feet. These may be applied as suckers to the valves of a bivalve shell. By slow, continual pressure the valves are eventually parted when the muscles holding them together become tired. The starfish is then able to turn its stomach inside-out over the soft flesh of the animal and slowly digests it. Starfishes also eat small crabs and other crustaceans, worms, snail-like molluscs (gastropods) and other animals, and often cause damage to oyster culture beds.

Crabs, lobsters, shrimps and prawns are also carnivorous. They feed on smaller crustaceans, worms, and young fish, and some on small bivalves.

1. A carnivore. *Starfishes use their tube feet as suckers to pull the shells of bivalves apart in order to expose the flesh of the bivalve.* 2. A suspension feeder. *This tubeworm collects suspended particles with its crown of tentacles.* 3. A detritus feeder. Tellina *is a burrowing mollusc. Its inhalant siphon (see text) is long and 'sucks' in particles which have settled on the sea floor.*

27

On the sea floor there is tremendous competition between the inhabitants of each part, for food, for places to live and so on. From a commercial point of view the competition of the invertebrate carnivores with the fishes is of considerable importance. Calculations suggest that nearly all the food that one would expect to be available to fishes is in fact consumed by invertebrate carnivores. Perhaps in future, methods will be devised of reducing the effect of the latter and so increase the supply of food available to the fishes, though of course some carnivorous fishes themselves feed on carnivorous invertebrates so that destroying the latter might well reduce the numbers of these fishes.

The type of bottom deposit is probably the most important factor affecting the distribution of the benthos. Mussels, like limpets, need to hold firmly onto rock. They attach themselves by long sticky threads called the byssus. Others can live in sand for they would suffocate in mud. One startling fact that has emerged recently is that the planktonic larvae of some bottom-dwelling animals are able to delay their development (when they reach a certain age), if they arrive at a part of the sea floor which is unsuitable: so they wait until they reach a suitable position.

But the temperature and salinity (saltness) of the water may also be important. The oyster requires fairly warm water for spawning (about 17—18°C.) but whereas the adult can live quite happily at lower temperatures the spawn will die. Low temperatures may also delay reproduction and slow down the development of the young. The longer their development is slowed down the greater chance they have of falling victim to predators. Salinity is fairly constant over the whole of the sea floor. It is only important as a factor in shallow water, where the tides and the outflow of fresh water from rivers may have an effect.

CHAPTER SIX

The Sea Shore

PERHAPS no place on earth is subject to more extreme changes than those experienced where land and sea meet. Here, the tides alternately cover and expose the shore twice every day. In spite of the ever-changing conditions, the shore supports, as a rule, a great wealth of animal and plant life. Every major animal group is represented, although some only rarely. In some groups, notably the periwinkles, one can actually observe stages in the evolution of terrestrial habits from marine ones. Undoubtedly *some* animals have completed this change although the evolution by way of fresh-water has been more important in the rise of land-animals.

The *shore* is defined as that region lying between the uppermost and the lowest limits of tidal movement. Tides are caused by the pull of the moon, and to a lesser extent, the sun. When

The Barnacle is a sessile (fixed) crustacean that feeds by 'combing' plankton from the water.

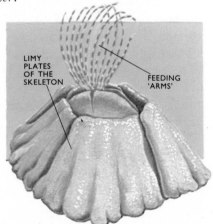

sun and moon are in line, their combined effect is stronger and the resulting fortnightly *spring tides* are of greater extent than the *neap tides* which occur every fortnight when the moon is pulling at right angles to the sun. The highest tides of all (and therefore the lowest low waters too) occur twice a year when the sun and moon are exactly in line. These periods are the

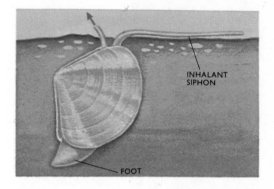

Tellina feeding by drawing sediment in through its siphon.

equinoxes and fall on or about March 21st and September 21st. The vertical range of tidal movement varies from a few inches, in the Mediterranean and other places, to more than forty feet off the coast of Nova Scotia.

There are thus a number of *zones* on the shore, distinguished according to the length of time that the land is exposed. The zone just above the true shore is often called the *splash zone*. It is never completely covered but, especially on rocky coasts, is frequently affected by salt-laden spray from the waves. This region has its own charac-

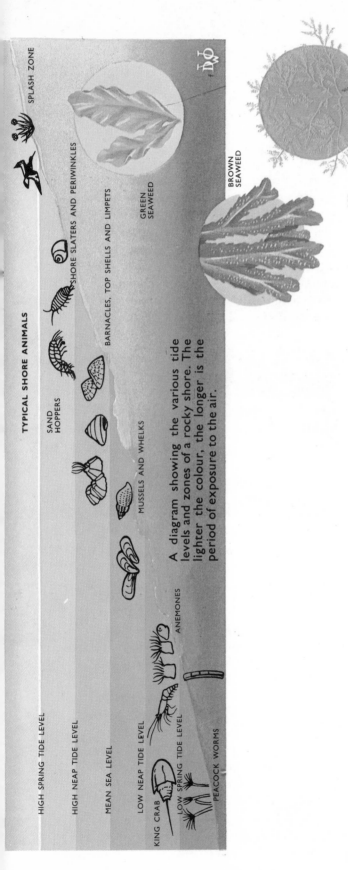

SPLASH ZONE

SHORE SLATERS AND PERIWINKLES

BARNACLES, TOP SHELLS AND LIMPETS

GREEN SEAWEED

BROWN SEAWEED

RED SEAWEED

TYPICAL SHORE ANIMALS

SAND HOPPERS

MUSSELS AND WHELKS

ANEMONES

KING CRAB

PEACOCK WORMS

HIGH SPRING TIDE LEVEL

HIGH NEAP TIDE LEVEL

MEAN SEA LEVEL

LOW NEAP TIDE LEVEL

LOW SPRING TIDE LEVEL

A diagram showing the various tide levels and zones of a rocky shore. The lighter the colour, the longer is the period of exposure to the air.

teristic plants such as Thrift or Sea Pink.

The type of shore varies enormously, even within a quite short stretch of coastline. The unending battle between land and sea results in erosion at one point and deposition at another. Where erosion takes place, cliffs develop, with rocky shores at their feet. The material eroded from the land is transported by off-shore currents and deposited elsewhere. Pebbles and shingle are deposited first, in the neighbourhood of the erosion site. Sand, made up of fine particles of silica and other material derived from many types of rock, is transported further by the water than are the pebbles. In very sheltered inlets, fine mud may be deposited, forming mudflats at low tide. This is especially noticeable around estuaries. Each type of shore has its characteristic animal life, admirably suited to the conditions.

A pebble beach, such as that derived from the erosion of chalk containing flints, is one of the most barren of all habitats. The rounded pebbles enclose large air spaces and cannot hold water between themselves. Any animals among the stones would quickly dry out at low-tide, or be crushed by the moving pebbles. Pebble beaches are usually fairly steep but lower down the beach the pebbles frequently give way to shingle and sand.

When exposed by the ebbing tide a sandy beach may look as barren as a pebble beach. Often the only evidence of life is a line of sea weed fragments and a few empty shells at hightide level. However, the small size of the grains means they can hold water by capillary action, even when some way above the tide level. This means, in turn, that animals can burrow into the sand and remain protected when the tide is out. Even only a few inches down they are immune from the effects of wind, rain and sunshine. The only animals capable of surviving on a sandy shore are those that can burrow when the tide is out. The commonest of these include worms, crustaceans and shellfish (molluscs). Most of them can feed only when the tide is in and they are covered with water.

Of the worms, perhaps the best-known are the lug-worms (*Arenicola*). These animals live buried and feed by eating large quantities of sand from which they extract any edible organic matter. Their presence can be detected by the 'casts' of undigestible material that they eject at the surface of the sand. Lug-worms are more common where there is plenty of fine organic matter i.e. where the sandy and muddy regions meet. Other worms live in tubes which they construct from particles of sand 'cemented' together with slime. They feed by use of tentacles that either pick up the sediment from the sea bed (*Lanice*) or strain particles of food from the water (*Sabella* – the Peacock Worm). The ragworms (*Nereis*) have powerful jaws and are carnivorous. They move about in search of food and at low tide may burrow or retreat with the waters.

The majority of shore-dwelling crustaceans are tiny animals living between the grains of sand but a number of larger ones are found on sandy and rocky shores. *Amphipods* (sand-hoppers) are often found among the sea weed litter at high tide level and at various levels down the shore. Some of those of the upper zones can stand only a limited amount of submergence and are almost terrestrial in habit. Shrimps are very common at and around low tide level but crabs are not common on sandy beaches except in the tropics. There, some of the crabs have developed almost terrestrial habits, even to the extent of climbing trees.

Bivalve molluscs are very common on both sandy and muddy shores. When the tide is out they burrow down but when covered with water they extend their breathing tubes (*siphons*) and begin to feed. The breathing organs (gills) also serve as food collecting devices. Water is drawn in through one tube, over the gills and out through a second tube. Particles of food are trapped in a stream of mucus and carried to the mouth. Some of the commonest bivalves of sandy or muddy shores are the cockle (*Cardium*), razor-shell (*Ensis*) and the pink or yellow *Tellina*.

Of by far the greatest interest to the naturalist is the rocky shore, for here are found a great many species and, what is more, they are normally visible at low tide. Limestones and slates are especially rich in species, for these rocks develop rough surfaces

Pomatoceros, *a tube-building worm, covers the rocks with its limestone tubes. It traps food in its tentacles.*

and many crevices in which animals can hide. They offer ample opportunity for plants to become attached and the plants themselves are very important in the life of the shore animals. The sea weeds clothe the rocks and protect them to some extent from the buffeting of the waves. They also provide shelter for vast numbers of animals, especially when the rocks are exposed at low tide. The weeds and the water they hold, adequately protect the animals from the drying effects of sun and wind. The shore slater (*Ligia*) is a typical member of the community.

Zoning is most obvious on the rocky shore because of the plants. On the upper shore the green sea weeds are common. They can survive even in the splash zone and can tolerate fresh water to some extent. Below them there are various zones of brown sea weed. The wracks (*Fucus*) tolerate varying periods of exposure, those with the least tolerance growing lowest on the shore. The long flat and wavy blades of *Laminaria* appear at about the level of the low spring tides. Red sea weeds are, in general, less tolerant of exposure and grow below shore-level and in rock pools.

Rock pools, where they occur, often contain animals which otherwise would be found only below low tide level. When the tide goes out on a rocky shore the animals must go with it or remain on the rocks and be able to withstand exposure. If they can do neither of these things they will perish. Thus the molluscs (e.g. periwinkles, whelks, mussels and others) are also zoned according to the amount of exposure they can stand. Some periwinkles live in the splash zone and cannot survive submergence. The existence of pools that never dry up means that various crabs, sea-anemones, fishes, and others can become established higher up on the shore than would otherwise be possible.

Feeding habits on the rocky shore vary just as on sandy ones. Sea-anemones, barnacles, tube-worms, mussels and others are fixed and capture what food they can from the water. Limpets and whelks, when submerged, move about in search of vegetable or animal food. Lower on the shore, where there is frequently a certain amount of sand, burrowing worms and molluscs may appear. They feed on the organic debris derived from the plants and animals higher on the shore.

Life on the Land

CHAPTER SEVEN

Rain Forests – The Plant Paradise

RAIN forests are found in a belt centred about the Equator. They grow in the best conditions for plant life that the Earth can provide. The equatorial temperature is high all the year round. The sunlight is bright and the rainfall is heavy – between 100 and 160 inches a year. As there is no cold season or winter, the plants can keep their green foliage permanently.

There are three separate rain forest areas – South and Central America, Central Africa and the Malaysia-Indonesia region. Each area has its own distinctive types of plants but the general appearance of rain forests is the same wherever they develop. Rain forests spread over immense areas but they are not continuous. Mountains, high plateaux, lakes, swamps, and rivers or just areas where soil is unsuitable, prevent them from covering the whole of equatorial regions.

Stories told by travellers and explorers have given the impression that the tropical rain forests are almost inpenetrable places; and that the air inside the dense undergrowth is heavy with the stench of rotting vegetation. This may be true for secondary jungles – clearings made by Man that have subsequently become overgrown. But for proper rain forest or primary jungle, it is the very opposite of the truth. The trees of rain forests have tall, slender trunks with foliage formed only at the top. The absence of branches lower on the trunk and the very small quantity of undergrowth present, makes rain forests easier to walk through than temperate woodlands. Usually the visibility is good enough to see for more than 20 yards. A few fallen leaves and broken branches may lie on the ground but the warmth and dampness of the tropics make decomposition too rapid for much dead vegetation to accumulate.

Rain forests are gloomy places. The thick, green foliage overhead shuts out most of the light. Even in the brightest sunlight only a few sun flecks can penetrate to the forest floor. This is the reason why so few plants can grow near the ground. Often the surface is bare enough for patches of red, slippery soil to show through.

Character of Rain Forests

In the forests of Europe and North

Rain forests grow in the equatorial regions of the Earth. Only in a few places do they penetrate outside the geographic tropics.

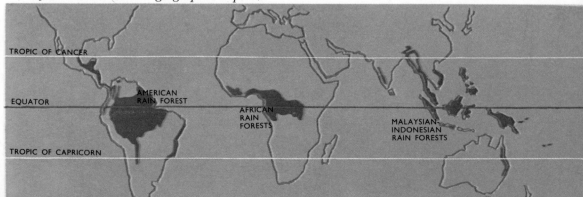

Deciduous forests in temperate zones shed their leaves during the winter.

The rain forests keep their luxuriant foliage all the year round.

America a few species of tree, or even just a single species, make up the biggest proportion of plant life. These woodlands are even referred to by the name of the most prominent tree – *oak forests* for instance, and *beech forests*. In rain forests there are usually more than 40 species of equally abundant trees; sometimes the number is as great as 100. One reason for this is that though plants in the tropics compete with one another for life, the warmth, abundant light and rainfall mean that there is not the same fight against difficult climates. Plants do not need to be adapted to meet some special condition and so far more different types can survive. Another reason is that today's rain forests have grown in the same positions for millions of years. This enormous length of time has enabled a great richness and variety of plant life to evolve.

A second feature of rain forest

Animal Life

Each layer of vegetation in rain forests supports its own distinctive animal life. Birds of prey nest in the top-most branches. Just beneath live monkeys and brightly coloured birds – parrots, toucans, and hornbills. These birds with the brilliantly-coloured epiphytic flowers and the metallic blues and greens of tropical butterflies make the tree-tops the most attractive parts of the rain forest. Some of the smaller tree-top animals develop flaps of skin between arms and legs enabling them to glide from branch to branch.

On the ground live small antelopes, wild pigs, tapirs, all kinds of lizards and snakes and in Africa and Asia occasional elephants. Leopards and other cats, large apes and frogs move between the ground and the lower trees.

The damp, humid conditions are highly suitable for frogs and toads; the largest known present-day forms live in rain forests. Many are tree-dwellers.

Rain forests are also the home of the largest living insects. Enormous flies and wasps, grotesque grasshoppers and huge beetles are among their inhabitants. The actual number of each different type of insect in rain forests is so large that it can only be guessed at.

35

HARPY EAGLE

A view from the top level of a rain forest in South America. The forest is divided into three main levels – the uppermost level receiving the most light. Many of the trees in the lower layers are young plants that have not yet grown to full height. The leaf shapes of rain forest trees are very much the same in shape with straight margins and drip-tips. The animal life varies with each layer. Birds of prey live in the top-most branches. A few

plants is that most of them have tough woody material. There are very few plants made up entirely of soft tissues (*herbaceous* plants). The jungle relatives of many small, herbaceous, garden plants are colossal trees. Bamboo for instance is a grass and yet it has a tough woody stem and grows to a height of 60 feet. Members of the violet family and the daisy family are large trees and a relative of the milkwort is a tough, woody twiner which climbs to a height of 200 feet. The wood gives support to a plant and enables it to grow high in the air without collapsing. This is necessary in rain forests, for overhead foliage is very thick. To obtain sufficient light, plants have to develop their own leaves as far off the ground as possible. Only a few shade-loving types can exist close to the ground.

The height of the tallest trees in rain forests is usually over 150 feet. There are two lower tree levels recognisable in rain forests. One level is made of trees approximately 100 feet high, the other is made of trees reaching about 40 or 50 feet. Of course, the smaller the tree the smaller the quantity of light it receives.

Not all jungle plants develop tall erect stems to reach the light. Many of them merely support themselves by climbing up the trunks and along the branches of other plants. There are thus enormous numbers of woody vines (*lianes*) hanging down from the tree tops. These show great variety in the methods they use to attach themselves to their supports. Some plants (*epiphytes*) grow permanently in the tree-

monkeys climb up during the day to look for fruit, but return at night to the level beneath. Flowers grow high in the air using deposits in crevices of the bark as soil. The lower canopy is bright with the colour of birds and butterflies. Most monkeys live at this level. The floor of the rain forest is gloomy. Many animals come down from lower branches to feed.

tops of rain forests without their root systems connecting them to the ground. Ferns and flowering plants as well as algae, mosses, liverworts and lichens live like this. It is the only way they can obtain enough light. The 'soil' necessary to give anchorage and provide water and mineral salts is made up of the remains of dead plants, that do not fall to the floor. Many of the plants have special adaptions to store water – rather like the cacti of desert regions.

Though there are very many types of 'jungle' trees, the appearance of the rain forest is surprisingly monotonous. One type of tree is very similar to another. They all have tall straight trunks with thin, light-coloured bark. Branches develop only at the tops of the trunk. The leaves are all large, leathery and dark green in colour with unbroken leaf-edges and a sharply pointed end or *drip-tip*. (The drip-tips are excellent adaptations for keeping the leaf well drained of water). The flowers, which form all the year round, are usually small, pale-green or white. Buttresses or woody side supports for the base of the trunk are common – especially in trees which do not have deep, strongly-binding roots. Where the soil is particularly water-logged and therefore poor in air, 'breathing' roots or *pneumatophores* grow up out of the ground and act as ventilating organs for the root system. The great similarity in appearance of unrelated plants is an example of *convergent evolution*; the different plants have been adapted to the same conditions by the development of similar structures.

Rain Forests Soils

In the tropics, decay is too rapid for much humus to accumulate. The absence of slowly decomposing organic matter means a low quantity of plant nutrients in the soil. Yet despite this, rain forests form the most luxuriant expanses of vegetation in the world. Why should this be? The answer is that though decay takes place very rapidly, soluble plant nutrients are nevertheless returned to the earth. The heavy rainfall quickly washes them down to lower levels of the soil but the absorbent activity of the roots equally rapidly takes them back again.

Plant nutrients of rain forests are therefore very much present; they are all stored away in the actual living vegetation. Some of the soluble nutrients may of course be completely washed from the soil, but this quantity is small and is easily made up by additional supplies which some very deep roots absorb from the parent rock a long way beneath the ground.

Rain Forests of the Past

Studies of fossil plants and fossil soils indicate that the tropical rain forests covered larger areas in pre-historic times than they do now. Probably, for instance, the African rain forest stretched eastwards and northwards to link up with the rain forests in Arabia and India. Subsequently, changes in climate and possibly Man's influence has limited the areas they cover.

Rain forests are known from Cretaceous times, 100 million years ago. Study of fossils of this age shows that Europe was probably covered in jungles greatly resembling those of the tropics today. The warm, wet conditions which existed during later Tertiary times were also suitable for growth of rain forests in Northern Europe.

Though the vegetation of jungles seems strange and weird to us who live in colder climates, it seems that the broad-leaved evergreen tree of the rain forest is the ancestor of most other plant types. Many of our temperate plants, in fact, still show traces of their tropical origins.

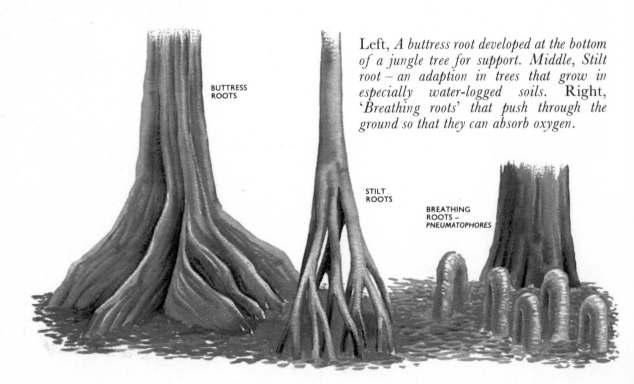

BUTTRESS ROOTS

STILT ROOTS

BREATHING ROOTS – PNEUMATOPHORES

Left, *A buttress root developed at the bottom of a jungle tree for support. Middle, Stilt root – an adaption in trees that grow in especially water-logged soils.* Right, *'Breathing roots' that push through the ground so that they can absorb oxygen.*

CHAPTER EIGHT

Polar Regions

POLAR regions occupy the extremities of the Earth's surface, the Arctic to the north and to the south the Antarctic. Because the Earth spins about the Sun with its axis tilted at $23\frac{1}{2}°$ to the vertical, the boundaries of the polar regions experience a day in mid-summer when the Sun never sets, and a day in the depths of winter when it never rises. These boundaries are the Arctic and Antarctic Circles and they occupy latitudes of $66\frac{1}{2}°$ north and south of the Equator respectively. Towards the poles, winter darkness increases while the summer becomes correspondingly lighter. At the poles themselves, the 6-month winter passes completely without sight of the Sun while during the 6-month summer the Sun is permanently above the horizon.

Polar winters, devoid of sunlight, are intensely cold. Temperatures of $-127°F$ ($-88°C$) in the Antarctic, and $-58°F$ ($-50°C$) in the Arctic, have been recorded. Even in summer the thermometers may often remain below freezing point, for though the Sun is perpetually shining, rays strike the Earth's atmosphere at an oblique angle and much of the warmth never penetrates to the ground. Also, where the surface is covered with white ice or snow, up to 90% of the heat is reflected.

The fundamental difference between the Antarctic and Arctic regions is that whereas Antarctica is a true continent ($1\frac{1}{2}$ times the size of Australia), the Arctic consists mostly of sea, with land made up of northern extremities of Europe, Asia and North America. Because of this, the Antarctic is by far the colder, for land is a poor heat conserver. The great expanse of water in the Arctic absorbs much heat in the summer and moderates the extremes of winter cold.

Land and sea inside the Arctic Circle. Only parts of Greenland are permanently covered in ice.

Life in the Arctic

Though the Arctic Circle is fixed at $66\frac{1}{2}°$ north, biologists make use of another, more northern arctic boundary – the line beyond which no trees will grow. Between this so-called *tree-line* and the shores of the Arctic Ocean are 5 million square miles of land. Most of it is low and flat – the *tundra*.

Tundra is frozen and bare for most of the year but during a brief summer interlude, a little of the frost thaws, loosening surface layers of soil. But at

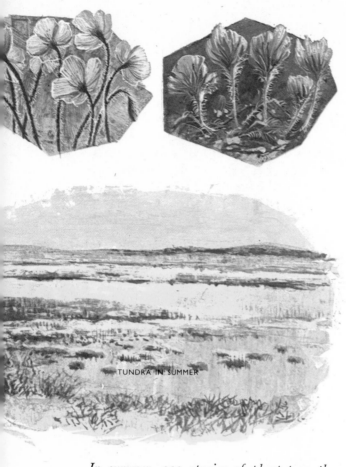

deeper levels the soil remains frozen and drainage is impossible. The melted ice is consequently trapped in shallow lakes and pools. For plant life this is just as well, for the tundra has a desert climate; only the equivalent of about 8 inches of rain falls a year.

The most successful and tenacious polar plants are the *lichens*. Lichens are part fungi, part algae. In the tundra they encrust bare rock surfaces even where the rocks are exposed to the wind. Near the tree-line the so-called 'reindeer-moss', in fact a lichen, is several inches tall and provides grazing for reindeer in the cold winter.

Stunted alders, birches and willows grow only a few feet high in the harsh climate but they may live for hundreds of years. In the summer, mosses are particularly abundant in marshy places while the grass-like *arctic cotton* and the numerous flowering herbs cover the damp, level ground.

With summer, animal life also returns. Insects are soon about and lemmings, (mouse-like rodents), shrews and voles appear from burrows under the snow where they have passed the winter; during the warm months they collect enough food to provide them for another cold season. Marmots, ground-squirrels and barren-ground grizzly bears come out of hibernation, their body temperatures returning from near-freezing point to normal.

Ducks, geese, plovers, cranes and numerous other birds fly up from the south. Ptarmigan (arctic grouse) which pass the winter in sheltered spots on the tundra build new nests on the ground. Herds of reindeer (caribou) return from the forests and musk oxen, which winter on high, wind-swept arctic plateaux, come down into the lowlands. In search of food

In summer, 900 species of plant turn the arctic tundra into a colourful landscape. The pools of water are formed by thawed ice. Below, the winter scene – the ground is encrusted with ice, the soil is frozen hard.

Lemmings are hunted by many arctic flesh-eaters. Here, the Snowy Owl – a wandering bird by no means confined to the tundra – has found a meal.

the flesh-eaters also arrive – on the land arctic wolves, weasels and foxes – in the air owls, skuas and ravens.

Polar bears – probably the best known arctic animals – wander over the pack-ice of the frozen Arctic Ocean. They mainly feed on seals. Their paws are rough for gripping the ice and a buoyant layer of fat helps keep them afloat when swimming.

Life in the Antarctic

Only about 3,000 square miles of the Antarctic continent's $5\frac{1}{2}$ million square miles remains free from ice. Most of this is concentrated in narrow strips about the coast. Like the Arctic, the Antarctic is a desert with only the

equivalent of few inches of rain a year. The summer temperature rarely rises above freezing point and fresh water pools are not so abundant as in the tundra. About 150 species of lichens survive, and a few mosses, but there are only three flowering plants.

The hardy lichens can grow on bare rock surfaces, even on mountain peaks far inland. In a state resembling death they can survive long periods of cold and drought. Their growing period may be just a single day in the year. Water is obtained from small quantities of melted snow and mineral salts from bird excreta carried in the wind as dust.

Small, simple algae which grow on

The white coats of Ptarmigans *and other animals of the tundra, change colour during the summer. The creatures are camouflaged all the year round.*

PTARMIGAN IN WINTER PLUMAGE

PTARMIGAN IN SUMMER PLUMAGE

damp, sheltered rock surfaces are found in great abundance. They may also be seen growing on the soft snow, tinging the white surface with greens and pinks. They may even survive in the ice of frozen pools. The three flowering plants – two grasses and a herb – are confined to the slightly wetter, warmer *Antarctic Peninsula*, a strip of land which straggles northwards almost to the 60° south latitude.

Vegetation is too sparse to support land mammals and the largest antarctic land creature is a wingless fly half a centimetre in length. In summer it clambers about on bare rocks and breeds in freshwater pools. (Birds and seals seen on the Antarctic continent gather food from the sea and are not true antarctic land-dwellers). Mites and spring-tails, depending upon mosses and lichens for food, come to life in the short summers but are dormant in the winter. In the pools of melted water, the largest animal is a freshwater crustacean, about an eighth of an inch long. There may also be protozoans, rotifers (wheel-animal-cules) and other simple creatures.

During the winter the flocks of Emperor penguins have the frozen antarctic shorelines to themselves.

SMALL EARS

RED FOX

ARCTIC FOX

The ears of the arctic fox are very small and reduce the surface area from which heat is lost.

Living in the Cold

The creatures best adapted to the intensely cold polar climates are the warm-blooded *birds* and *mammals*. Excessive loss of heat to the cold world outside is prevented by thick fur, feathers or layers of fat and oil.

Some warm-blooded creatures can conserve heat by keeping the extremities of their bodies as much as 50°F below the normal temperature of their bodies. For example, the legs of reindeers, huskies, and many birds, and the flippers of seals operate quite effectively at low temperatures. The arteries carrying warm blood to the limbs intermingle with veins returning cooled blood and consequently heat from the warm blood is transferred and saved.

The body temperatures of cold-blooded creatures closely follow the outside climatic temperature. The severe cold of polar winters would kill them or reduce them to a sluggish, inactive state. A few insects – parasites – manage to survive amidst the fur or feathers of warm-blooded polar creatures. Other insects, together with protozoans, rotifers and numerous other simple creatures, survive cold spells by suspending their living activities – they appear to die. But with warmer conditions, they come to life again. This curious state, so closely resembling death, is called the *anabiotic* state.

Polar plants must be hardy for they have to survive long periods of inactivity during the cold winters. They are generally all small, growing in clumps, close to the ground. Here they escape icy winds and obtain what heat there is from the Earth's surface. In the Arctic, the warmer summers give a much greater variety and profusion of plants than in the Antarctic, though the eight weeks or so when the temperature remains above freezing point is a very brief opportunity for plants to grow, store food, and reproduce. Many no longer flower and seed but multiply by sending out runners and stolons. One advantage of polar summers is that light is plentiful and plants can photosynthesize throughout the day and much of the night.

They come, not for feeding, but to reproduce. In temperatures around −50°F the male penguin incubates the single egg laid by the female. The egg is supported upon the webbed feet and warmth is provided by the thick feathers of the lower abdomen.

The continent of Antarctica is almost completely covered in ice. In places the ice may be more than a mile thick. The tree line is far to the north, running through the island of Tierra del Fuego. The simple animals and plants which permanently reside in the Antarctic are nearly all confined to coastal areas. The three flowering plants are found only on the Antarctic Peninsula.

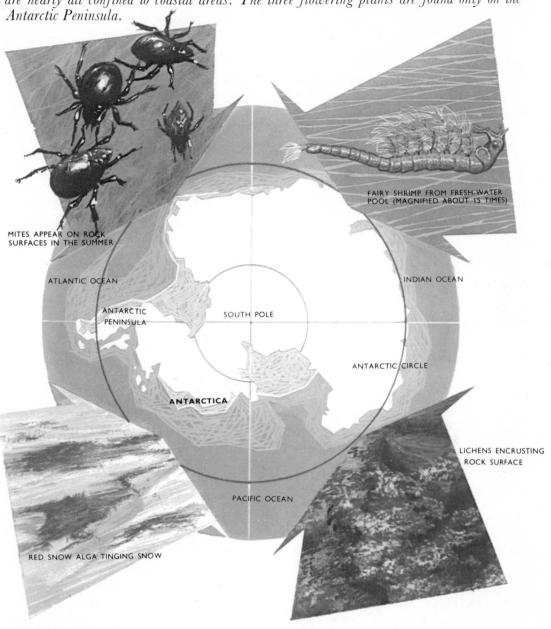

FAIRY SHRIMP FROM FRESH-WATER POOL (MAGNIFIED ABOUT 15 TIMES)

MITES APPEAR ON ROCK SURFACES IN THE SUMMER

ATLANTIC OCEAN

INDIAN OCEAN

ANTARCTIC PENINSULA

SOUTH POLE

ANTARCTIC CIRCLE

ANTARCTICA

LICHENS ENCRUSTING ROCK SURFACE

PACIFIC OCEAN

RED SNOW ALGA TINGING SNOW

CHAPTER NINE

Deserts

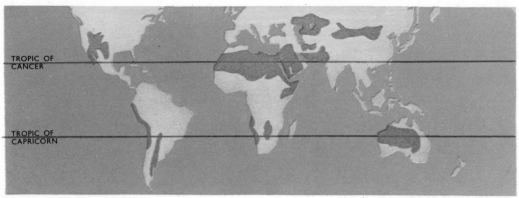

Deserts of the world. Some are far inland or in the rain shadow of high mountains. Others near the sea are deprived of water by cold currents offshore. The Sahara Desert is the largest with an area of 3,500,000 square miles.

HOT, dry deserts, with an average rainfall of less than 10 inches a year, cover more than 14% of the World's land surface. If the neighbouring, semi-arid steppes, with their slightly higher falls (10–20 inches) are included, the estimate of these largely unproductive areas rises to 28% of the surface or 16 million square miles.

Yet even though Man cannot cultivate crops in desert regions, these parched lands are not entirely barren wastes. Life is adaptable and has overcome the hazards and problems imposed by acute water shortage. Plants flourish in the most unlikely spots – a sudden downpour of rain and a bare, sandy surface is transformed into an exotic colourful patch of flowers. Again, what appears to be a deserted waste during the heat of the day, at dusk becomes alive with small scuttling animals.

Where are the Deserts?

Deserts are found in two broad belts encircling the Earth. The approxi-mate centres of the belts are the two geographic tropics – the Tropic of Cancer (north of the Equator) and the Tropic of Capricorn (south of the Equator).

The dryness of some deserts, for example the *Gobi Desert* of Mongolia, is due to their remote positions far inland. The winds have lost nearly all their moisture before these parched regions are reached. But more important for desert formation are the currents of cold water off the shores of many land masses. The cold water cools the air, which in turn lowers the amount of moisture that can be carried inland by winds.

The reason why deserts are not only dry but intensely hot is that the lack of water in the atmosphere enables 90% of the Sun's heat to penetrate to ground level; only 10% is absorbed or deflected by dust and clouds. At night, in contrast, 90% of the ground's heat is lost to the upper air and temperatures fall rapidly.

44

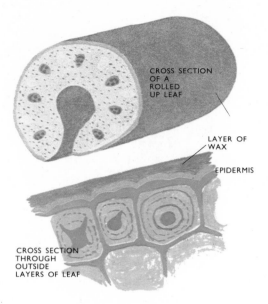

CROSS SECTION OF A ROLLED UP LEAF

LAYER OF WAX

EPIDERMIS

CROSS SECTION THROUGH OUTSIDE LAYERS OF LEAF

Leaves may roll up into tubes reducing the area from which water can be lost. Coatings of wax also stop excessive evaporation.

The sparse rainfall may be seasonal in some regions. North Africa, for instance, has a Mediterranean climate with dry summers and mild, damp, winters. Northern parts of the Sahara desert therefore receive most of their rain in winter. But the rainfall of many

Many shrubs and cacti absorb water over a wide area by means of shallow, spreading roots.

desert areas remains unpredictable and some spots may go ten years or more before a sudden, torrential downpour floods the hard, scorched ground.

Plant Life

Many desert plants survive droughts as resistant seeds with tough protective coats. When rain does eventually fall, the seeds quickly germinate. These plants are called *drought evaders*. They avoid the problem of water shortage – and have no special adaptations such as wax-coated leaves, water storage organs or deeply penetrating roots. Growth is rapid, flowers are produced and more seeds form. The cycle is over in less than 6 weeks.

Perennial plants likewise flourish during the rare rainy spells but for the rest of the time they must endure the harsh dry climate. These are the *drought resistors*. Any water that does become available must be absorbed and conserved. Many different adaptations are found to do this.

The cacti of American deserts are great hoarders of water. When mois-

The large desert trees obtain water using deep-penetrating tap roots.

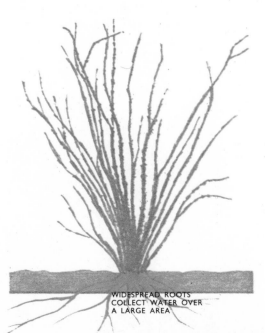

WIDESPREAD ROOTS COLLECT WATER OVER A LARGE AREA

DEEP-PENETRATING TAP ROOTS.

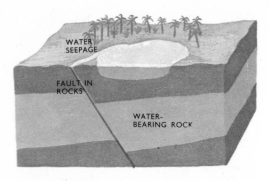

The occasional oasis of deserts is formed at points where water in underground layers of rock can penetrate to the surface. Below, shifting sand dunes occupy only a small percentage of desert. The rest is bare rock or has a firm sandy surface.

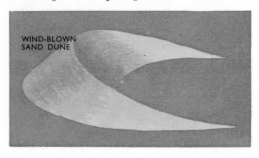

ture is plentiful it is quickly taken up by the shallow, widespread cactus roots. The stem of the plant is used as the storage organ, the pleated surface filling out as the water is absorbed. As in many desert plants the leaves are absent, so reducing the surface area through which water can be lost. Photosynthesis takes place in the surface cells of the stem. The spines of cacti (outgrowths of the stem), discourage browsing animals from destroying the plants for the sake of their water supply.

Another adaptation characteristic of the larger desert trees such as the *Mesquite* of America and the *Acacia* of Africa, is the very deep tap root. It may penetrate to a depth of 100 feet or more in search of moisture. With a reasonable supply of water assured, the leaves are often found to be unprotected against water loss.

Smaller shrubs have shallow, widespread roots, deep tap roots or both. Because the competition for water is strong they are usually found well separated from each other. The leaves are sparsely distributed and are often coated with wax, which prevents excessive loss of water through evaporation.

The *Paloverde* tree of Africa has leaves less than a millimetre across and even these small structures tend to fall off the branches in severe droughts. The leaves of some desert plants are no longer used for photosynthesis but are modified into prickles for protection.

About a third of all desert perennials store water in underground structures – roots, rhizomes, bulbs, tubers and nodules. The plant structures above the ground die off in very dry weather leaving their portions underground to produce new flowers and seeds when the rain returns.

Animal Life

When the rain does fall in deserts, while many plants renew their activity, millions of insect eggs and cocoons also burst open releasing adult beetles, wasps, moths, ants, crickets and locusts. Many of these creatures are very important as fertilizers of the desert flowers. Their life is soon over

The cactus stores water in pulpy tissue in its stem. Cells in the stem also photosynthesize.

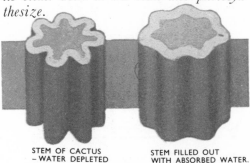

STEM OF CACTUS
– WATER DEPLETED

STEM FILLED OUT
WITH ABSORBED WATER.

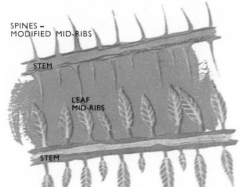

SPINES – MODIFIED MID-RIBS

STEM

LEAF MID-RIBS

STEM

In desert plants the midribs of leaves may become adapted as thorns. Skin outgrowths and branches may also form prickles.

but they leave behind a new supply of eggs to resist the drought. Spiders, scorpions and centipedes – usually covered with thick hair or skin – are quite common and after flooding, swarms of small shrimps are found in the temporary puddles. The eggs from which they hatched may have lain in the desert for twenty years.

Temporary puddles are also the homes of frogs and toads. They quickly breed and when the water evaporates, the parents and young burrow in the mud to avoid the heat. They line their burrows with mucus to prevent water loss and are often equipped with some structure for digging.

Species of lizard, snake, and tortoise

Swollen corns, tubers and roots may store water in times of drought.

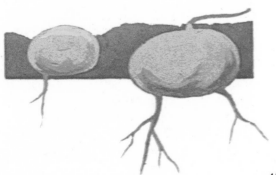

To keep body temperatures from rising too high, many desert animals cool themselves by using water from their own bodies. Mammals have sweat glands which secrete a salty liquid on to the skin surface. Subsequent evaporation lowers the body temperature. Reptiles and birds do not have sweat glands and can only lose water by panting. By burrowing in the ground during the hottest parts of the day however, most reptiles, amphibians, and small mammals avoid losing water.

Water may also be used up in excreting nitrogen-containing wastes produced by the breakdown of proteins in the body. Birds and reptiles avoid this water loss by excreting almost solid *uric acid*. But the *urea* excreted by mammals must be passed from the body in solution. The loss of water is kept to a minimum by concentrating the urea so that it makes up more than 20% by weight of the solution. Plant-eating mammals do not produce much urea, but flesh-eaters, with a largely protein diet, need a constant supply of water to dissolve their excess waste.

Sufficient water may be obtained by desert creatures, in the foods they eat. Insects for instance are made up of between 60 and 85% of water. Even the very low water content of seeds (less than 5%) may be enough for some small burrowing rodents. Flesh-eaters, birds and larger browsing animals need a good water supply, and do not stray out of reach of water holes. The camel however can survive long periods without drinking. It probably stores water in spaces between its tissues and may receive a supply of *metabolic* water by breakdown of fat in its hump.

live in deserts. Their plates or scales are good adaptations for stopping water escaping. They cannot survive in temperatures of more than about 45 °C and so during the heat of the day, burrow in the ground or seek the shade. Special valves close the nostrils and prevent sand from entering.

The majority of desert mammals are small burrowing rodents that feed mostly on seeds scattered about the desert floor. Nearly all deserts, how-

JERBOA

TUFTED TAIL FOR BALANCE

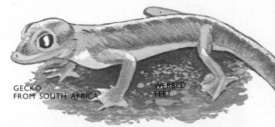

GECKO FROM SOUTH AFRICA

WEBBED FEET

This gecko has webbed feet – not for swimming in water but for walking over the sand. The spade-digger toad has a horny pad on its rear foot for burrowing in the mud during drought.

NORTH-AMERICAN SPADE-FOOT TOAD

HORNY PROJECTION OR 'SPADE'

With powerful back legs and a long tail, which can be used for balancing, the jerboa is typical of the 'jumping rodents'.

ever, have their own specialized jumping 'rodent' equipped with strong rear limbs for rapid propulsion. America has the kangaroo rat, Africa and Asia the jerboa and the gerbil and Australia the marsupial (pouched mammal) kangaroo mice.

Browsing mammals such as small species of deer are not so widespread, for they must drink at least once a day,

and remain confined within easy reach of a water-hole. Zebras in the deserts of South-West Africa detect water that lies underground and construct their own drinking place by excavating with their hoofs.

CHAPTER TEN

Mountain Life

EXPLORING the Andean mountains of South America, Alexander von Humboldt, German explorer and traveller, climbed to a height of 18,096 feet above sea level. The year was 1802. The mountain was Chimborazo – a volcano located in Ecuador. At the time, this was the greatest height known to have been reached by Man.

But Humboldt's achievement was more than a mountaineering triumph.

Throughout his climb he had taken detailed scientific readings with the most up-to-date instruments then available. He found that as the altitude increased so the temperature and pressure decreased. What is more, he noticed how the changes in physical conditions were reflected in the plant life.

Luxuriant tropical rain forest in the plains gave rise to forests of giant ferns on the lower slopes. In turn the ferns

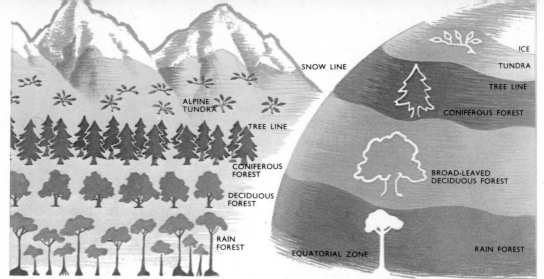

Mountain vegetation changes as the altitude increases. In tropical regions there is a gradation from rain forest in lowlands to tundra towards mountain summits. This variation in the types of plant closely follows the pattern of vegetation belts from the Equator to the North Pole. Decreasing temperature is the common factor and accounts for the similarities.

gave way to a belt of broad-leaved deciduous forest. Then, at higher levels, followed coniferous forest with fir and pine. Higher still it became too cold even for conifers to survive. Here were only stunted shrubs and small plants. Finally a region was reached which was permanently covered in snow and ice. There were no plants growing here at all.

Mountain vegetation changes going upwards in precisely the same way as plant life changes over the surface of the globe. Passing from the Equator to the Poles there is an identical succession – rain forest, deciduous forest, coniferous forest and tundra. The reason is that in both leaving the Equator and climbing a mountain, temperatures fall. Polar regions are colder than equatorial regions because the axis of the Earth is tilted. Mountains are cold because air at high altitudes is rarefied and dry; the lack of moisture in particular means the air cannot retain heat. On a summer day temperatures may rise to over 100°F. But with nightfall, the heat absorbed

Outside tropical regions, some of the belts of mountain vegetation may be missing. Rain forests are generally absent. Further from the Equator, deciduous forests disappear and eventually even coniferous forests may be absent.

Many alpine plants seem more related to arctic plants than the lowland forms in their vicinity. But how did they get there? The Alps for instance are nearly two thousand miles from the arctic tundra. Twenty thousand years ago ice covered much of North-West Europe and certainly penetrated as far south as the Alps. When the temperatures rose and the ice retreated northwards the plants which are the present day arctic forms moved northwards as well. Only on the mountain tops were the cold-weather plants able to survive. They represent isolated colonies of the original Ice Age vegetation.

by the ground is quickly lost to the atmosphere again.

The mountain plants making the lower zones of vegetation are almost identical with lowland counterparts, although particularly long roots give support on sloping exposed surfaces. But in the alpine tundra zone, above the timber line, there are characteristic mountain or *alpine* plants many of which are found nowhere else.

These high mountain slopes provide very severe climates. Like the arctic tundra, long bitter-cold winters are broken by very short summers. In addition the slopes are exposed all the year round to strong gusts of wind which remove warmth from the plants.

Living under the same difficulties, different plants have often evolved along similar lines. They are all small, growing close to the ground. In this way, they avoid the full blast of the wind. Also, because they are so close to the ground, the plants gain what heat there is from the Earth itself. Plants standing just an inch or so above the ground may have a root a couple of feet in length. Roots have to be long to give good anchorage on sloping ground. They must also be efficient water absorbers for drainage quickly takes place downhill and the winds have a strong drying action.

Many alpine plants are cushion-shaped and though they are small, the foliage is widespread and thick. The tangled leaves and stems act rather like the hairs of mammals or the feathers of birds. They trap a layer of air inside which is both moister and

In summer the snow melts, providing moisture. Though the days are hot, the nights are below freezing and the wind is fierce. The cushion pink is a typical alpine plant with a cushion-shaped tangle of stems and leaves. Hairs on leaves and stems capture warm, moist layers of air. Flowers are often deep coloured — perhaps they help to absorb heat.

Winter in alpine tundra. Most animals either hibernate or retreat from the exposed slopes into the shelter of the trees. The timber line marks the approximate boundary beyond which trees are generally unable to grow. Here a solitary pine has taken root a little further up the slope. The wind has killed the branches on the windward side.

CUSHION PINK

ALPINE PLANTAGO

BLUE GENTIAN

Sheep, goats and types of antelope are characteristic mountain animals. A variety of species occur throughout the uplands of the world. Left, the Rocky Mountain goat is in fact an antelope. With the polar bear it is the only animal to retain a white coat throughout the year. It lives permanently on the high slopes of the Rocky Mountains and neither migrates nor hibernates in the winter. Right, Alpine Ibex – a wild goat found in a few places in the Alps; species of Ibex are also found in Asia and North Africa.

warmer than the surroundings.

Nearly all alpine plants are perennials – that is they live for more than a year. Annual plants are a great rarity for conditions are too severe for a life cycle to be completed each year. Usually growth is very slow. Ten years may pass before a plant has stored up enough energy to flower and produce seeds.

During the winter a blanket of snow insulates the plants from biting sub-zero temperatures. The plants remain dormant but possess enough energy stored as food to grow anew in the spring. Sometimes the snow does not melt and the meagre supplies of food must keep the plant alive for two years

Renewed growth or germination may begin before the snow has actually melted. Light from the sun can penetrate through as much as a foot of snow. Though the summers are short, very high temperatures, well over 100°F may be reached during the day. Then at night, the dry air gives out all

its heat and temperatures quickly fall to below freezing point. Plants counter the strong drying conditions by possessing wax-coated leaves or a covering of hair. The wax prevents excessive loss of water, the hair traps a layer of moist air about the plant. While the sun is shining, as much energy as possible must be absorbed. The leaves consequently are rich in chlorophyll.

When plants at last flower, there are very few insects about to cross pollinate them. The wind becomes an important pollinating agent carrying pollen dust from one plant to another. Some flowers avoid the problem of cross fertilization by self-pollination. Pollen produced by the stamens fertilizes the carpel – borne on the same flower.

As in arctic **tundra regions** lichens – plants made up of algae and fungi – prove the most hardy and resistant of all vegetable life. They encrust exposed rocks in places where no other plants can grow. They grow very slowly but may live for hundreds of years.

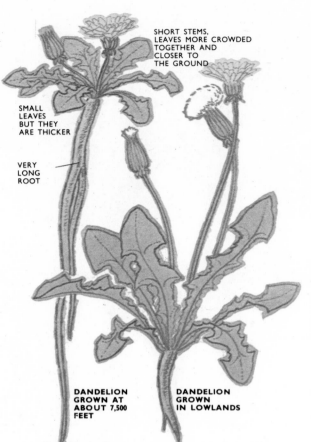

SHORT STEMS, LEAVES MORE CROWDED TOGETHER AND CLOSER TO THE GROUND

SMALL LEAVES BUT THEY ARE THICKER

VERY LONG ROOT

DANDELION GROWN AT ABOUT 7,500 FEET

DANDELION GROWN IN LOWLANDS

Lowland flowers grown on mountainside show marked changes in their appearances. The different conditions particularly of light and temperature cause them to assume many of the characteristic structures of true alpine plants.

Animal Life

Because such a wide variety of temperatures is experienced on mountains, only warm blooded creatures – mammals and birds – are really successful. They keep at a constant temperature which is maintained by using up energy in their bodies. In contrast, cold-blooded creatures depend upon the surrounding climate for their body temperatures. The excess of heat or cold is usually fatal for them.

Most conspicuous of upland creatures are the large plant-eaters, sheep, goats and chamois. During the sum-mer they lead a wandering existence high on the mountains. During winter, most of them migrate to the forests on the lower slopes. Here they obtain food and shelter. Their large size is a protection against cold. In comparison with the volume of their body, the surface area of skin – the heat-losing surface – is small. Heat loss is further reduced by the growth of thick fur.

Sure-footed, wary and with a good turn of speed, the mountain herbivores

As altitudes increase mountaineers climb more and more slowly. The air becomes thin (*rarefied*) and the oxygen necessary for body activities is consequently less plentiful than at low levels. What is more important, the atmospheric pressure falls; 15 pounds per square inch at sea-level, at 18,000 feet it has dropped to half this quantity. As a result there is a much reduced force pushing the oxygen from the atmosphere into the lung.

Yet at heights between 14,000 and 18,000 feet – sufficient to leave lowlanders groping for breath, some races of men live and work quite normally. Special adaptations in their bodies have overcome the difficulties.

Chests are barrel-shaped and capable of great expansion. Inside, the lungs are larger than normal. The surface area at which oxygen exchange can take place is thus increased. Red blood corpuscles which carry the oxygen in the blood are not only larger but more numerous; they may be 20% more numerous than in the blood of lowlanders.

Mountain peoples tend to be fairly short and squat. Their compact bodies further improve the blood circulation for blood does not have to be pumped so far each time it passes around the body. The extremities of the body such as the hands and feet have large numbers of direct channels linking the small arteries with small veins. The circulation is quickened and ensures the tissues receive a good oxygen supply and can maintain a steady temperature. Thus mountain people are particularly resistant to frostbite and can walk barefooted even in snow.

The pika – close relative of the rabbit. During the summer it stores grass as a winter food – a natural hay-maker.

Snow-Leopard – the chief flesh-eater of the Himalayas. During winter it follows its prey to the lower slopes.

Alpine marmots eat the leaves and roots of mountain plants. In winter they hibernate in communal burrows, under the snow.

ALPINE MARMOT THERE ARE SPECIES IN ASIA AND NORTH AMERICA

PIKA FOUND ON MOUNTAINS IN NORTH AMERICA AND ASIA

SNOW LEOPARD THE AMERICAN EQUIVALENT IS THE PUMA

are much more formidable animals than their lowland counterparts. They usually can out-manoevre, out-run, sometimes out-fight wandering flesh-eaters – wolves and wild cats – that follow them. The hooves have pincer-like toes for obtaining grip. They also have raised heels with soft hollowed pads which grip like suction caps.

Smaller animals are less conspicuous but even more abundant. They are principally rodents – squirrels, and marmots – though rabbits and hares manage to live on the slopes as well. A wide variety of plant food is eaten. Some of the food may be stored away to provide for the lean winter months. When the snow falls many of the creatures burrow underneath; insulated against the frost and equipped with good supplies they are quite comfortable until the following spring.

An alternative method of escaping the cold is to hibernate. The ground squirrel does this. Immense quantities of food are eaten in the summer and stored in the body as fat. Then, inside a burrow lined with grass the creature falls into a deep sleep. The body temperature falls and the heart beat slows down. But enough food is present to keep the creature alive until the following spring.

Many birds inhabit the mountain uplands. Nesting on inaccessible ledges, their chicks are free from attacks by predators. But the range of the parent bird is by no means confined to the mountain slopes. Birds are so mobile that they can cover great distances in all directions.

Some of the world's largest flying birds live on mountains. The wing-span of the American Condor for instance is often ten feet. The birds make use of the upcurrents of air created by the mountains. Some of the birds – the swift for instance – are small and feed upon insects. Insects and spiders are the only cold-blooded creatures found. Many are blown high onto the mountain slopes by the wind but some do manage to live permanently there – eating plants, scavenging or feeding off other insects. Because they take their temperatures from the surroundings they emerge only when the temperature rises. At other times they remain in a lifeless state in cracks in the ground.

CHAPTER ELEVEN

Communities of Plants

AN oakwood in springtime: close to the ground clumps of moss, white anemones, lesser celandines, winter aconites, and thick green spreads of dog's mercury; above, an undergrowth of stouter woody shrubs such as hazel, hawthorn and sloe; higher still branches of the oak trees themselves, supported on tough rigid trunks. All these plants are growing on a similar sort of soil; all are subjected to the same sort of climate. Together they make up a recognizable *community* of plants.

The term *plant community* is of great use in plant ecology. It can be applied to any collection of plants which make up a distinct type of vegetation – from woodlands to the scant plant growth on the flanks of a sand-dune. For greater precision of meaning, according to the scale of the plant community, a number of other terms can be used. A *plant formation* refers to a community in very broad terms. The great belts of vegetation found throughout the world – the rain forests, desert vegetation, deciduous forests, coniferous forests – are examples. Studied in greater detail each plant formation breaks down into a number of subsidiary categories. Oakwoods, for example, are a smaller community falling within the larger community of the deciduous forest plant formation. For such a community, dominated by a single species (i.e. the oak tree) the term *consociation* is used. If there are two or more species of equal importance, then the community is called an *association* (e.g. mixed oak-ash woods). Finally, very small but distinct communities may occur inside associations or consociations. Within an oakwood for instance, there may be a local predominance of ash trees. This lowest category is referred to as a *plant society*.

Distribution of Communities

Why are rain forests found only in tropical regions? The occurrence and distribution of any plant community rests with three sets of factors. There is the *climatic* factor – including the influence of sunlight, temperature, wind, rainfall and humidity; there is the *soil* or *edaphic* factor – the composition and properties of the soil supporting the plant community. And there is the *biotic* factor – primarily the influence of the animal population on the plant community.

The climatic factor is without any doubt the most important of the three. It is the world-wide variation in climate that gives the characteristic vegetation belts or plant formation. No matter what the soil is, a rain forest would never grow in Western Europe. Rain forests need moisture, warmth and strong sunlight *throughout* the year and only in the tropical regions are those needs satisfied. Western Europe, however, with its warm moist summers and coldish winters is the ideal for deciduous forest.

The soil or edaphic factor has a strong secondary influence on plant

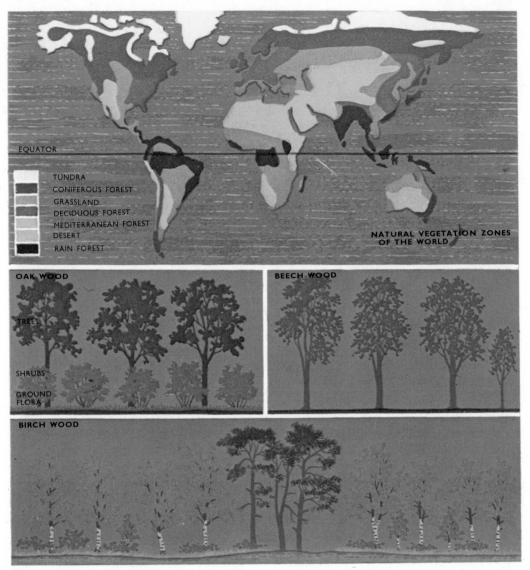

EQUATOR

TUNDRA
CONIFEROUS FOREST
GRASSLAND
DECIDUOUS FOREST
MEDITERRANEAN FOREST
DESERT
RAIN FOREST

NATURAL VEGETATION ZONES
OF THE WORLD

OAK WOOD

TREES

SHRUBS

GROUND
FLORA

BEECH WOOD

BIRCH WOOD

Above, plant formations of the world. Climate is the controlling factor. Middle left, oak-wood consociation *showing stratified structure of community. Right, beech* consociation – *the deep shade cast by these trees prevent lower levels of plants from forming. Below, a plant society – localized occurrence of pines within a predominant birch forest.*

communities. The types of associations and consociations within a plant formation are largely determined by soils. Within the deciduous forest category for example, oakwoods usually monopolize the lowlying woodlands. The reason is that oaks are suited to the moist heavy clays generally forming low areas. Beech woods favour light, shallow, limey soils and hence grow scattered over downs and limestone hills. Shallow sandy, well-drained soils favour the growth of birch trees and pines. Oakwoods may be found here as well, but this oak tree – the Durmast oak or *Quercus petraea* – is a different species to the Pedunculate oak (*Quercus robur*) of the

Duneland plant communities are tolerant of poor soil with low mineral content. Here marram grass, sea spurge and sea holly begin colonizing shifting sand. More mature 'fixed' dunes are seen in the background, where plant succession has proceeded.

lowlying clay soils.

The biotic factor theoretically means the action of all organisms on the plant community, including the influence of the plants upon one another. But usually the phrase is taken to mean the effect of the animal population alone. It includes soil-dwellers such as earthworms, bacteria and viruses, the pollinating insects, destructive grubs, the browsing and grazing animals such as deer and rabbits, the seed-dispersing birds and of greatest importance of all – Man himself.

Man's impact on plant communities with his axe, plough and herds of grazing animals is immense. Many centuries of agriculture have reduced the forests in many places to scanty woodlands. In their places are highly artificial plant communities – fields of crops and pastures carefully tended by Man to prevent unwanted, useless plants (weeds) from encroaching.

Structure of Communities

For sheer size, the tree dominates the plant kingdom. Its tough woody

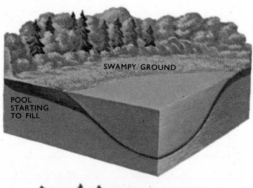

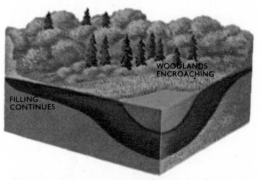

Obliteration of a pool. Swamp plants are succeeded by shrubs and small trees. The plant succession will end in a climatic community of woodland.

56

Plant communities evolve. From simple beginnings they may pass through a series of changes (the *plant succession*) until they reach an advanced woodland community. Imagine an area of land cleared of its top-soil by a bulldozer. The first plants to re-colonize the area are hardy pioneers requiring little in the way of nourishment from the soil. They include the lowly algae, the mosses and the lichens. With the successive death of a few generations of these pioneer plants the soil has become richer in humus. In come new species of plant — mostly annuals with efficient dispersal mechanisms — that now can flourish in the better soil. They replace the pioneers, but in turn may largely be replaced by later perennial plants.

Shrubs and small trees appear. With enough time, larger trees may become established and begin to dominate the community. The final result is a stable community in which no further great changes take place. The end-point is reached and this community is called the *climax community*.

But the climax community is only stable so long as the surrounding conditions remain constant. Changes in the climate, in the soil, or changes caused by Man or other animals can upset the stability. The dominant species may decline and disappear and new species take over. Such an event has taken place in Western European woodlands since the end of the Ice Age.

receive the maximum amount of sunlight available. Considerably less light penetrates the trees' foliage to reach the smaller shrubs, and less still reaches the herbaceous plants growing near to the ground and the mosses actually in contact with the earth.

This layering effect or stratification is a characteristic of all plant communities. In woodlands it reaches its greatest development with four 'stories' — trees, shrubs, herbs and mosses. Outside the woods, the layering may not be so complete yet nevertheless is still present. Grasslands, for instance, consist of an upper layer of tall grasses and herbs while beneath are rosette plants and short grasses. The tree as a dominant plant in a woodland community strongly influences the lower levels of growth. Beech trees cast a very deep shade. Consequently, in such a wood, the vegetation nearer the ground is scanty or absent altogether. Oaks and ashes casting less shade enable far more abundant and varied undergrowths and ground floras to flourish.

Apart from the differences in light intensity, slight variations can also be detected in the air's carbon dioxide, oxygen and water content at each level of a plant community. Thus superimposed on the broad climate of the community as a whole, each plant layer has its own peculiar *micro-climate*.

stem enables leaves and flowers to open scores of feet above the ground.

But trees dominate in one other way. Their leaves, supported high in the air

CHAPTER TWELVE

Peat Bogs

PEAT is an accumulation of partly decayed plant material. It tends to form wherever waterlogging or acidity slows down bacterial decay. Peat is first stage in the formation of coal. However, it would take millions of years under the pressure of overlying rock to turn into coal. In many regions peat is cut and used as fuel. It is not very efficient however.

Large tracts of Ireland, Northern Britain and Northern Europe are covered by *blanket bog*. Rainfall exceeds evaporation and the peat tends to blanket all level ground and shallow slopes - hence the name 'blanket-bog'. Bogs also occur locally where drainage is hindered and acidic soil water collects. If the soil water is alkaline and contains plenty of minerals, a *fen* usually develops.

Fen vegetation consists mainly of reeds and sedges. The peat formed in a fen is usually black and fairly well decayed: the alkaline conditions allow bacteria to act on the dead plants. Bog peat, however, is brown and individual plant fragments are often visible. The acid surroundings prevent bacterial action. The major constituents of bog peat are the bog-mosses (*Sphagnum* species) together with several grasses and sedges. Heathers frequently grow on established bogs. Insect-eating plants such as sundews are common. They supplement the meagre nitrogen supply on the bog by capturing insects.

Bog-mosses are interesting because they are able to alter their surroundings to suit themselves. The cell-walls, even in the dead plant, are able to adsorb metallic ions (e.g. calcium) from the surrounding water and release hydrogen ions to take their place. This makes the surroundings acidic, so that the moss grows more rapidly. Decay slows down and peat begins to build up. However, if there are too many metallic ions in the original surroundings the moss becomes saturated with them and cannot grow. It grows best where there are few mineral salts in solution.

Sphagnum grows at the tips of the shoots. These die off lower down and become compressed into peat. There is thus always a living carpet on the bog surface. The leaves contain many large empty cells and these hold water rather like a sponge. This is true of the dead parts, too, and so a peat bog carries its own water supply which can be drawn upon by the living moss

Sphagnum growing on a raised bog. Several species are tinged with red. The blade-like leaves are of cotton grass.

The History of many European Blanket Bogs

Trees existed in an earlier drier period.

As the climate grew wetter, bog moss began to grow. Young trees did not grow to replace fallen ones.

Blanket bog covered the region until it began to break up under Man's influence.

at the surface. Walking on a bog causes the whole surface to tremble and usually brings water to the surface.

Several species of *Sphagnum* grow on the bog. The early ones are often those that can stand more alkaline conditions. Gradually, as they create acidic conditions, they give way to those less tolerant of alkaline conditions. *Sphagnum* species also vary in their liking for water. The surface of a bog is rarely flat but covered in mounds and hollows. In the hollows there is usually water and water-loving *Sphagnum* species. Gradually the hollow is filled with peat and other species take over, forming mounds. The higher the mounds get, the drier they become and eventually heather grows on the top. Peat formation is slow then but in the new hollows it is more rapid and the cycle starts again. The alterna-

tion of mound and hollow can be clearly seen on present bog surfaces. Sections through the peat also show the alternation. Each type of plant produces a different type of peat and they can be seen following one upon the other. This mound complex is seen on blanket bog but is even more characteristic of *raised bog*.

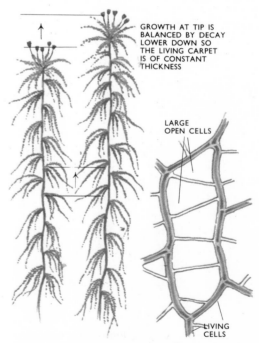

GROWTH AT TIP IS BALANCED BY DECAY LOWER DOWN SO THE LIVING CARPET IS OF CONSTANT THICKNESS

LARGE OPEN CELLS

LIVING CELLS

Sphagnum or bog moss. The base of the plant dies off as the tip grows up. Therefore there is always a living carpet on top of the peat. The large open cells of the leaves hold lots of water.

59

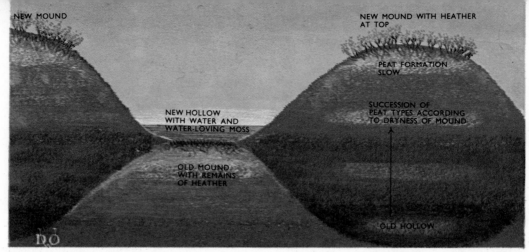

Diagram to show how a hollow becomes a mound and vice-versa during the growth of a bog.

Raised bog develops frequently on top of fen peat. As the latter builds up and the soil water loses its influence, *Sphagnum* can colonise the surface and turn it into acid bog. Raised bogs are typically domed in the centre; here, the effect of alkaline ground water is least and growth is greatest.

As the peat increases in thickness, it depends more and more on rainwater. It gets increasingly acid and poorer in mineral content. The tendency is to dry out and peat formation slows down. Human interference and grazing have destroyed the *Sphagnum* of many upland bogs in Britain and the peat is now covered by heather and cotton grass. In this condition it is more of a moor than a peat bog.

The history of a bog can be discovered by boring down through the peat. If the bog started off as a fen, the borer will bring up samples of fen peat and probably lake mud with mollusc shells. Boring through blanket bog will probably show that the peat rests directly on mineral soil.

The lack of decomposition in peat bogs means that many things are preserved. Pollen grains are very important in the study of bogs. The grains remain intact and it is possible to determine the type of plant from which they came. If, at a particular level, the grains are mainly alder and oak, it can be assumed that the climate was wet and bogs were forming rapidly. Archaeological remains also help to date the peat deposits and carbon-14 dating is providing an estimate of the actual age of bog peat.

Although raised bogs are fairly stable and there may be many feet of peat, blanket bogs do not go on growing indefinitely, especially when they are on a slope. When they reach a certain thickness (depending on the slope and the type of peat) they tend to slip. Gullies form and water runs down, washing the peat with it. *Bog-bursts* occur sometimes when whole slopes of peat move down the hillside. They have been known to overwhelm whole farms.

Many raised bogs are found in regions of basic rocks. The section shows how, when fen peat had built up to above the water level, Sphagnum moss colonized the surface and formed a bog. Fen plants (reeds) still grow at the edges where the water is alkaline. The section of a blanket-bog (right) shows that the peat rests directly on the soil or rock.

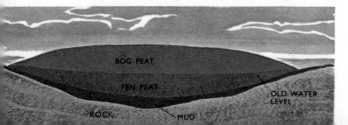

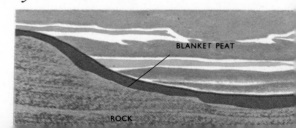

Life in Fresh Water

CHAPTER THIRTEEN

Pond Life

RAIN falling upon the land runs over and through the soil and finds its way into streams and ponds. During its journey, the water dissolves a great deal of material and carries more in suspension. These materials include nitrates from decaying organisms, mineral salts from the rocks, and oxygen and carbon dioxide from the atmosphere. These are vital and valuable plant foods and it is not surprising that plants have colonised freshwater wherever possible and that the plants have been closely followed by animals. Life in freshwater presents a number of problems that have been solved in various ways. Running and still water present different problems and support different types of community.

The natural history of a pond depends very much upon the local geology. Ponds in regions of volcanic rocks or on sandy heaths are notably poorer in vegetation and animal life than ponds fed by water from chalk or limestone regions. The acidity of the rocks (and therefore the water) is also important in determining the future succession of vegetation in the lake or pond.

A pond or lake with rocky shores provides little root-hold for vegetation but a lowland pond in clay or river deposits shows distinct grouping of the plants. Various rushes, yellow irises and marsh marigolds grow in the damp ground around the edges. Right at the water's edge, and often growing out into the water are such plants as the common reed (*Phragmites*) and the reed-mace (*Typha*). Truly aquatic plants are found further out in the water. They may be rooted with floating leaves (e.g. water lilies) or with submerged leaves (e.g. Canadian pondweed) or with both types of leaf (water crowfoot). A number of plants (e.g. duckweed and frogbit) are free-floating and may cover the whole surface of small ponds. Lastly there are the minute floating plants – the *plankton* – that form the first links in the food chains of the community.

The plants provide food and shelter for the animal inhabitants and also, through the process of photosynthesis, provide oxygen which dissolves in the water. The dissolved oxygen is very important, not only for the living organisms but also for the decomposition processes on the floor of the pond. The weediest ponds are usually the ones with the most animal life but they also produce the most waste material. Plants can grow only in the upper layers where there is light. A deep or very dirty pond will have no plants at the bottom and, unless there is a good circulation of water, very little oxygen. The processes of decomposition will quickly use up what oxygen is present, and little animal life will survive. Ponds under trees are rarely of any interest to the naturalist. Shade prevents plant growth and the accumulation of leaves uses up what oxygen can dissolve in the water. The pond is black and barren. Only those animals, such as the Rat-tailed maggot, which can feed on the foul material, and get

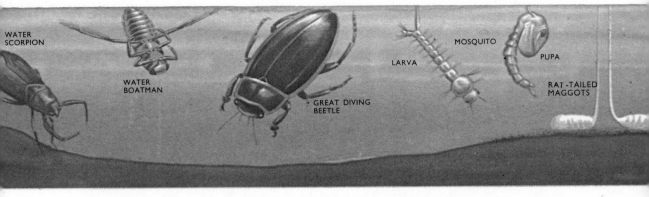

WATER SCORPION

WATER BOATMAN

GREAT DIVING BEETLE

MOSQUITO

LARVA

PUPA

RAT-TAILED MAGGOTS

Various insects and the methods by which they obtain oxygen from the surface.

oxygen from the surface, can survive.

The Animal Life

Representatives of almost every major group of animals can be found in fresh water and every region of a pond has its characteristic inhabitants. The surface of the water, although no different in composition from the rest, acts like a very thin skin and is able to support some small animals. The pond-skaters and whirlygig beetles are often found skimming across the surface in search of unfortunate insects that have fallen on the pond. Whirly-gigs have divided eyes: the upper parts are thought to be able to see in the air and the lower parts down through the water. On the underside of the surface film, black planarian worms glide along, small snails hang and mosquito

larvae take in their air supply.

Obtaining oxygen is one of the main problems to be overcome by animals living in the water. Small animals, such as *Hydra* and water-fleas, get sufficient by simple diffusion from the water. Larger animals require special breathing organs. Fishes have *gills* which absorb oxygen directly from the water. Some insect-larvae also have gills e.g. dragonfly and cad-disfly larvae. These animals can survive only where there is an adequate oxygen supply in the water. Many animals, however, have re-invaded water from the land and are still air-breathers. They have to come to the surface periodically for air. Such animals include water-beetles, water-bugs, some fly larvae, pond-snails and the semi-aquatic mammals such as

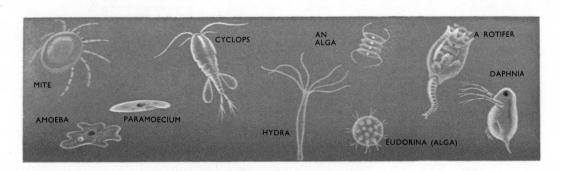

MITE

CYCLOPS

AN ALGA

A ROTIFER

DAPHNIA

AMOEBA

PARAMOECIUM

HYDRA

EUDORINA (ALGA)

Some small pond-living organisms.

63

beavers and otters. The air-breathing habit means that the animals can live in poorly oxygenated water – provided that there is sufficient food.

A few sweeps with a small net in a good pond will bring up a fascinating array of small animals which can be studied in small dishes or aquarium tanks. Probably the most numerous (apart from the microscopic protozoans) will be the tiny crustaceans – *Cyclops* and *Daphnia*, for example. These are in all parts of the pond. They feed by straining minute particles and organisms from the water. Water Boatmen (*Notonecta*) and the related bug, *Corixa*, are often caught as they swim around in search of food. The Water Boatman swims on its back by using its long back legs. It attacks a variety of living things including fish, and can inflict a painful nip on an unwary finger. Perhaps the most ferocious insect in the pond is the Great Diving Beetle (*Dytiscus*). This large green and brown beetle will attack quite large fish. Bugs and beetles are insects and have a delicate network of tubes (*tracheae*) in their bodies for carrying oxygen to the tissues. Some water-living ones, including those just mentioned, come to the surface to replenish an air-supply that they carry under a fine coat of hair or under their wing cases. This air supply is in contact with the openings of the breathing tubes. Other insects (e.g. *Nepa* – the Water Scor-

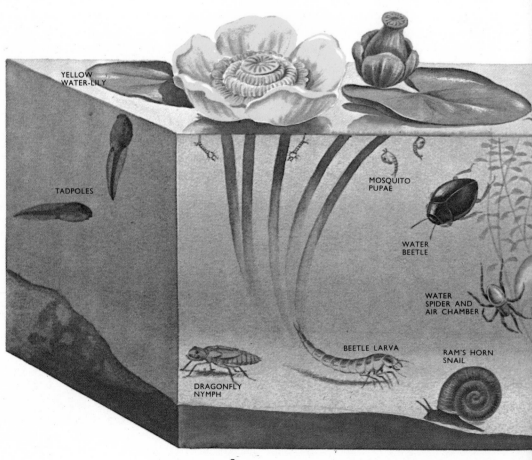

YELLOW WATER-LILY

TADPOLES

MOSQUITO PUPAE

WATER BEETLE

WATER SPIDER AND AIR CHAMBER

BEETLE LARVA

RAM'S HORN SNAIL

DRAGONFLY NYMPH

pion and the Rat-tailed maggot) have long tubes (siphons) that reach the surface and obtain air in that way.

Samples taken from the weedy areas may contain *Hydra*, attached to the plants, and numerous water-snails e.g. *Limnaea* and *Planorbis*. Caddis larvae and water spiders may also be present. Water Snails are descendants of land forms and still breathe air. They periodically come to the surface film and open their 'lungs' to the air to replenish the supply.

In the mud at the bottom of a pond may be found more snails and the freshwater mussels. The latter do not breathe air. They draw a current of water over their gills and extract both food and oxygen from it. These molluscs are very useful for keeping artificial ponds relatively clear. They consume much of the bacteria and algae. Other bottom-living animals include planarian worms, leeches and a little worm called *Tubifex*. The latter lives half buried in the mud, and waves its body about to create a flow of water. This brings it a supply of oxygen which it absorbs with the help of haemoglobin in its blood. It is thus adapted for living where the oxygen content is low. The few examples mentioned here show but a small proportion of the interesting features of pond life. The ease of collecting and studying pond animals makes pond life an ideal subject for the amateur naturalist.

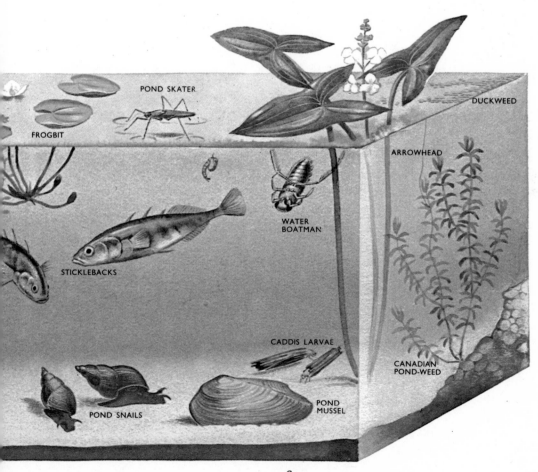

CHAPTER FOURTEEN

Rivers and Streams

THE character of a river changes considerably between its source and its mouth. The speed of the current and the nature of the bottom deposit vary from one part of a river to another. They are important factors which severely limit the distribution of the animals and plants within it. Few plants can gain a foothold where the current is swift and where sand or mud is not deposited. Of the animals, strong swimmers and flattened and streamlined forms with means of clinging to stones and the like are best suited. On the other hand, where the current flow is negligible, sand and mud will be deposited, plants will have sufficient material in which to root and a variety of animals (especially burrowers) will be able to make a living.

Chemical factors are also of importance. Occasionally a stream may be acid and poor in dissolved salts, barriers that few animals are able to overcome. Where large quantities of sewage are piped into a river, decomposition may so deplete the oxygen content that all plants and animals are killed.

Numerous attempts have been made to describe a typical river but this is extremely difficult, for each has its own characteristics. Some may rise on a mountainside and the headstream, though not containing much water, will be extremely fast flowing. Others may appear as springs at the bottom of a chalk hill and from there flow gently to the sea. However, one classification of the habitats is described below. Some rivers lack some of the divisions and local conditions (e.g. waterfalls) may upset the sequence. The five divisions are:— *Headstream, Troutbeck, Minnow reach, Cyprinoid reach* and *Pleuronectes reach* (the latter is present only in rivers that enter the sea).

Headstream

This, the upper region of the river or stream, generally occurs in high ground. Usually it is short with a shallow, fast flowing trickle of water from the source. This may be a spring or melting ice, for example. Its bottom is generally rocky and, although it is shallow, its temperature is low and it has little power of erosion.

Mosses and liverworts thrive in the damp conditions. Despite the fact that food is relatively scarce, the headstream has a surprisingly varied population. There are numerous protozoans, and wheel animalcules (rotifers). Of the crustaceans, the Freshwater Shrimp (*Gammarus pulex*) is often found. It 'prefers' shallow running water, rich in oxygen.

The young stages (*nymphs*) of a number of insects are adapted for life in fast-moving water. Common are the nymphs of some mayflies. The adults are extremely short-lived – from a few hours to two or three days – but the nymphs may take two years from the time of hatching to reach the adult stage. Many adult mayflies fall victim to fish, especially

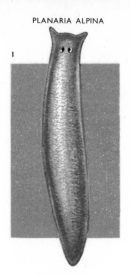

PLANARIA ALPINA

1

ECDYONURUS

2

ANCYLASTRUM

2

EPHEMERA

3

trout. The artificial 'flies' of Trout fishermen are models of several species of mayfly. Older nymphs have gills along each side of their body. These obtain oxygen from the water. *Baetis* is frequently encountered.

A few caddisfly larvae that build light cases are encountered – *Stenophylax* and *Agapetus*, for example. The latter's case has a flat side, with two openings in it, and a curved side. It is built of tiny stones. *Agapetus* hides under stones.

Nymphs of the stoneflies *Leuctra* and *Nemoura* are frequently found. They are not good swimmers and live mainly by crawling on the underside of stones, pressing their flattened bodies close to the stone surface so that the water current does not lift them up and wash

them away. Besides the snail, *Limnaea trunculata* (or Dwarfed Limnaea), a number of so-called *relict* forms may be found. These are animals which were of widespread occurrence during the Ice Ages. As the ice receded, however, the number of habitats in which they could survive was seriously reduced.

In moist ground along the edges of the headstream, the larvae of several species of crane flies or daddy-long-legs are found.

Troutbeck

The troutbeck is a more permanent channel downstream of the head-stream. The volume of water is greater and the current is swift. The bottom is either rocky, or strewn with stones and boulders, and may also contain some gravel. Erosion is considerable and there may be some deposition at the bends. The water is extremely cold and the quantity of dissolved oxygen high. There is little vegetation but, where bottom deposits occur, Water Crowfoot may gain a foothold. As the name suggests, the trout is the typical fish of this region.

The nymph of the mayfly, *Ecdyonurus*, is broad and flat. The strong claws at the tips of its large flat limbs

TUBIFEX IN MUD TUBES

4

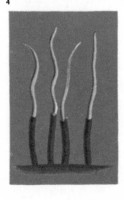

HYDROBIA

5

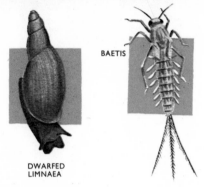

BAETIS

DWARFED
LIMNAEA

enable it to cling tightly to the surfaces of stones. Stonefly nymphs, for example *Perla* and *Isoperla*, are frequently found. Several web-spinning caddis-fly larvae inhabit the troutbeck. *Hydropsyche* builds a net of silk threads on the underside of stones. Plants and animals caught in the net are seized by the larva and eaten. *Stenophylax* and *Agapetus* also live in this region. Larvae of the Black-fly (*Simulium*) inhabit the Troutbeck, attaching themselves by means of a tail sucker to stones in the centre of the stream where the current is fastest. They can also spin strands of silk, just as a spider can, to avoid being washed away and so they regain a lost position.

The Wandering Snail, *Limnaea pereger*, common also in ponds, is frequently found, as is the River limpet, *Ancylastrum*. Leeches, too, and flatworms live in the troutbeck.

The troutbeck is the home of oxygen-loving animals. The speed of the current is such that they have to cope with considerable stresses. All are beautifully adapted, either because they are streamlined or flattened (e.g. *Ecdyonurus*), they have suckers or filaments for adhesion (e.g. *Simulium*), they hide under stones (e.g. Miller's thumb), or they are powerful swimmers (e.g. Trout).

Minnow Reach

The Minnow is the characteristic animal of this region. The current is slacker, erosion less pronounced and the fall of the river is less rapid. There are usually a number of stones on the bottom, for the coarser grits are deposited. These act as barriers to other material floating downstream, and pools often form at the edge of the stream. The water temperature varies considerably with the time of year, often being high at the edge.

TROUT

68

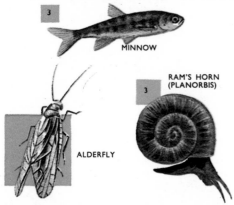

3 MINNOW

5 FLOUNDER

GAMMARUS

ALDERFLY

RAM'S HORN
(PLANORBIS)

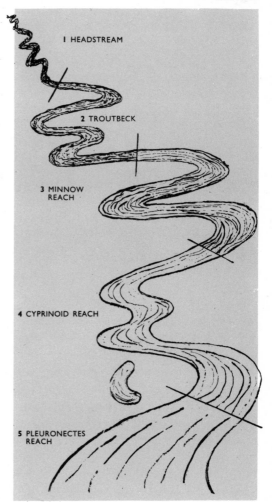

1 HEADSTREAM

2 TROUTBECK

3 MINNOW
REACH

4 CYPRINOID REACH

5 PLEURONECTES
REACH

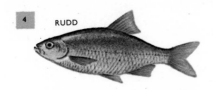

4 RUDD

The Wandering Snail, Pea-shell Cockle (*Pisidium*), Fountain Bladder Snail (*Aplecta*), and Ramshorn Snails (*Planorbis*) are common molluscs. There are many young stages of caddis-flies and dragon–flies, and numerous flatworms. In the pools, and at the edges, there may be sufficient sediment for some burrowing forms. The nymphs of the mayfly *Ephemera* live in burrows, but the water has to be sufficiently muddy for the light intensity to be low. Light is harmful to them. Some of the familiar blood-worms (larvae of the midge *Chironomus*) build tubes of mud and feed on debris in the bottom deposit. Larvae of the alder-fly (*Sialis*) are often found and water bugs may occur if the water is fairly slow-moving. Salmon spawn where there are beds of gravel, and on bends, where deposition is sufficient, the ammocoete larvae of lampreys often live.

Cyprinoid Reach

The current of this region is slow and there is considerable deposition. The river meanders and gravel carried down in floods is deposited on the slack-water side of bends. The stream slowly changes course by continual deposition and erosion, often leaving ox-bow lakes. Its temperature is variable.

Water plants are abundant, especially at the edges, and often the surface may have a complete covering. Reeds occur where the banks slope gently. In the centre of the river typical running-water forms live, but the edges and quiet back-waters have a lake-like fauna. Burrowing forms often predominate where the water is turbid (e.g. *Ephemera*, various worms – *Nais*, *Tubifex* – and blood worms). Molluscs include species of Pisidium, *Sphaerium* (Orb-shell Cockle), the Swan Mussel (*Anodonta*) and Fresh-Water Mussel (*Unio*). Plankton is not common and the nekton consists almost entirely of fish of the family Cyprinidae such as Carp, Bream, Tench and Rudd.

The Cyprinoid reach is a region of great variation, often upset by man's influence, as in areas where meadow farming is practised and the stream is channelled off over a wide area. The back-waters tend to have a richer fauna.

Pleuronectes Reach

This is the tidal region of a river. Such factors as temperature, salinity, and current direction vary tremendously.

Of the animal community only a few species are native to slightly salty (brackish) water. They include two species of the freshwater shrimp *Gammarus duebeni* and *G. zaddachi* and a flatworm (*Procerodes*). A brackish water form of Jenkins's Spire Shell (*Hydrobia*) is also common.

The region is named after the flounder (*Platichthys*) a member of the family *Pleuronectidae*. This fish abounds in muddy estuaries, leaving the rivers for the sea in the spring in order to breed. This fish and many others pass through the Pleuronectes reach on their way from the river to the sea, or in the reverse direction, to breed; for example the Trout, Eel, Salmon and Smelt. Several species of *Coregonus*, relatives of the salmon, also frequent brackish water.

Living Together

CHAPTER FIFTEEN

Symbiosis

MANY close associations exist in Nature between quite unrelated living things. These may be between one plant and another, between a plant and an animal, or between two animals. The closeness of the association and the amount of 'give and take' varies considerably. For instance one 'partner' may be so specialised that it is unable to exist on its own. Such is the case with many parasites. Tapeworms, for example, have no gut, they rely on their host to provide them with already digested food. Their relationship is a *parasitic* one—the tapeworm gives nothing to its host, and the latter may suffer considerable harm. Other associations may be looser – the sharing of a burrow, for example – and are said to be *commensal*. There are some very close associations between two organisms to their mutual benefit, which is called *symbiosis*.

Perhaps the best known example of symbiosis is that between the hermit crab and a sea anemone (e.g. *Adamsia*). The anemone is often found attached to the shell in which the hermit crab lives. In their long history hermit crabs have developed the habit of sheltering within the empty shells of molluscs such as periwinkles and whelks. The hind portion of the body has lost its hard covering and would otherwise be unprotected. As the crab gets bigger it outgrows its shelter and so has to find a new one. Often, a sea anemone attaches itself to the crab's shelter and it may

envelop part of the crab's own shell as well. The growth of the crab and anemone keep pace with each other and the crab has no need to change its shell – more and more of it is sheltered by the anemone. As the crab moves about in search of food the anemone is brought into contact with a greater supply of food and the crab no doubt gains a certain amount of defence from the anemone's stinging cells.

Many protozoans and single-celled algae live symbiotically with animals. Symbiotic plant cells are particularly common in planktonic shelled protozoans—the foraminiferans and radiolarians—and in corals and other many-celled animals in tropical seas. It is possible that such associations have arisen because of the relative lack of minerals in the surface waters of warmer seas. Radiolarians have a frothy layer of protoplasm outside the main mass of protoplasm. Within the froth are embedded a number of tiny yellow plants. These obtain shelter and have a ready supply of food in the form of the waste materials that the radiolarians produce. The oxygen that the plant cells release in their food-making processes is available to the radiolarians and possibly food substances as well. By using up the waste materials alone the plants render a useful service to the animals.

Many coelenterates and some flatworms have green algae (Zoochlorellae) living in their tissues. *Hydra viridis*, a coelenterate commonly found in freshwater, owes its green colour to the many algal cells in its tissues. Corals (particularly reef corals) and sea anemones also have symbionts in their tissues. Recently it has been shown that in reef corals the algae are of no food value and the amount of oxygen that they release bears no relation to the needs of the coral. They are certainly of value in using up the waste substances produced by the coral, however, and it is probable that

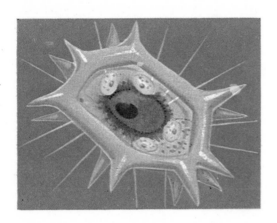

(Above) Root nodule bacteria live symbiotically in tiny nodules on the roots of legumes. They fix atmospheric nitrogen, building up organic nitrogen-containing molecules, which the legume can obtain from them through its vascular tissues. The bacteria obtain sugars in return. (Left) A radiolarian containing symbiotic yellow cells.

the same applies for sea anemones and for *Hydra viridis* too. The algae obtain shelter and the waste substances for food.

A most interesting association is that between *Carteria*—a plant-animal —and the flat-worm *Convoluta*. When very young, the latter lives the life of a normal flatworm, feeding in the same way as other free-living forms. However, at an early age it obtains a 'stock' of symbionts, loses its gut and becomes completely dependent on them for its food supply. The symbionts obtain a supply of carbon dioxide and nitrogen-containing waste materials. They are also brought out into the light by the animal at appropriate times. The flatworm is supplied with oxygen and food and

has its waste materials removed.

Symbiotic micro-organisms—bacteria, fungi (yeasts) and protozoans— play an important role in the lives of many insects. They may be harboured in the gut or in special cells (*mycetocytes*) which are often grouped together to form organs called *mycetomes*.

Most termites have symbiotic protozoans in the hind part of the gut. These actively ingest the wood particles that the termite has eaten and break them down, releasing substances that the termites can absorb. Experiments show that the termites depend on the protozoans for much of their food, and when the latter have been removed, so that the termite has none in its gut, it loses weight rapidly and dies.

One wood-eating termite grows only when the wood on which it feeds harbours a fungus population. Some wood-eating cockroaches have protozoans and bacteria in their gut and certain scarab beetle larvae house bacteria that digest cellulose.

Some biting lice and several sucking lice have mycetocytes containing bacteria, and many bugs have mycetomes that contain bacteria and yeasts. It has been shown that in some female beetles the symbionts are smeared on to the eggs from special sacs as these are laid. The beetle grubs become infected after hatching when they eat the egg shells.

Mammals harbour vast populations of bacteria in their stomachs and intestines. Ruminants such as cows and sheep have special chambers in the stomach in which the bacteria live, feeding on cellulose in the grass on which their hosts feed. By their acti-

vities the bacteria produce simple organic acids (e.g. acetic acid) from the cellulose, which the cows and sheep can absorb through their gut wall. Bacteria also produce vitamins (e.g. B_{12}) in the gut. This may be the only supply of some of these essential food substances. In rabbits and horses the symbiotic bacteria are harboured in chambers or *caeca* of the large intestine.

There are several well-known associations between birds and game animals. Cattle egrets, for example, are often seen in the company of buffalo and elephants. They flourish on the insects kicked up by the feet of these animals. The egrets appear to be aware of approaching danger rather more quickly than the game animals and it is likely that their actions in this respect serve to warn their larger companions.

A frequently observed phenomenon

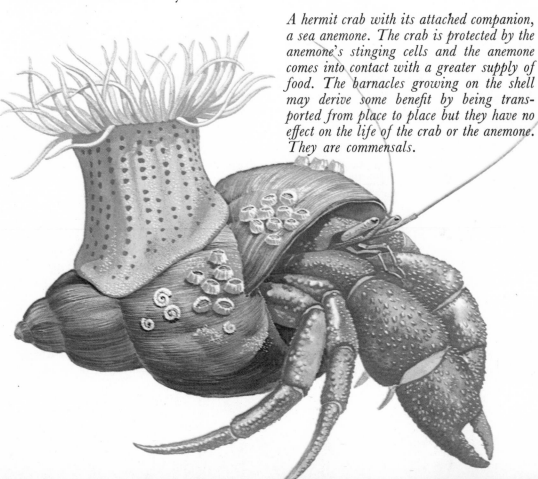

A hermit crab with its attached companion, a sea anemone. The crab is protected by the anemone's stinging cells and the anemone comes into contact with a greater supply of food. The barnacles growing on the shell may derive some benefit by being transported from place to place but they have no effect on the life of the crab or the anemone. They are commensals.

in Africa is that of oxpeckers running over the backs of hippopotami and rhinoceroses. These birds rid their partners of injurious and annoying insects and in doing so obtain a ready supply of food.

In the plant world there are many examples of symbiosis: root-nodule bacteria infect the roots of legumes (e.g. Clover); some orchids and heathers form close associations with fungi (called mycorrhizas) as do forest trees such as the Beech and Pine.

Lichens are peculiar plants formed by the union of a fungus and an alga. They play an important part in the formation of soils, being the first to colonise rocks. The substances that they produce dissolve the rocks away, forming the fine particles that are washed down by rain to form soils. They consist of algal cells embedded in a weft of fungus threads. The algae that occur within lichens are very similar to free-living forms but the fungi are unable to lead an independent existence. The alga is protected and supplied with moisture while the fungus absorbs the food materials made photosynthetically by the alga.

Cattle egrets and oxpeckers accompany the larger game animals. The former feed on the insects stirred up by the animals' hooves and may warn them of approaching danger. Oxpeckers rid their hosts of parasites and obtain food in the process.

CHAPTER SIXTEEN

Parasitic Animals

A VAST animal world exists hidden on the surface of other living things or concealed inside them. This is the world of parasites – organisms that live on or in other organisms and take food from them. Examples are fleas, lice, tapeworms and liver flukes. Each of the animals (and plants) that we see around us has several different parasites so that there are in fact more parasites than hosts.

A parasite lives in close contact with its host and is completely dependent upon it for food. Unlike the symbiotic creatures described in the previous

The human body louse. Note its flattened body, clawed limbs, and the absence of wings.

The head or scolex of a tapeworm showing the hooks and suckers.

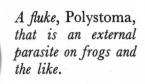

A fluke, Polystoma, *that is an external parasite on frogs and the like.*

chapter, parasitic organisms give nothing in return – the host may, in fact, be severely harmed. Parasitic organisms are unable to live a free life for long. This is because most parasites have become thoroughly adapted to a parasitic existence. In doing so they have often lost the power of locomotion, their sense organs are reduced (they do not meet the changing conditions that a free living animal does in exploring its environment), the gut may be reduced or absent and the reproductive system has become greatly developed. This is of great importance for, in order that the race shall survive new hosts must be contacted. The greater the number of offspring the better is the chance that this will happen. This adaptation may be compared with that of parasitic flowering plants, such as dodder, in which the vegetative parts are very reduced. The energy saved in not building these parts is used in the production of numerous tiny seeds. It seems probable that the ancestors of present day internal parasites lived on the outside of their hosts. Over millions of years and by way of many minute structural changes they became adapted to a life inside their hosts. In this way the habits of today's internal parasites evolved so that some now invade the innermost parts of the host.

Inside another animal a parasite has many things to gain. It is generally immune from the attacks of other animals and from inclement

Parasites and their Hosts

Most parasitic animals belong either to the Protozoa (single-celled animals) or to the various groups of worms, particularly the flatworms and roundworms, though more and more tiny crustacean and insect parasites are being discovered.

All the groups of vertebrates, and many invertebrates too, are known to be attacked by protozoans of one kind or another. *Monocystis*, for example, lives in the reproductive organs of earthworms absorbing the fluid surrounding it through the surface of its body. Its life cycle is complicated but it is probably passed on to other worms when the latter eat soil containing bird droppings, the infected worm having been eaten previously by the bird.

Malaria parasites and trypanosomes (both similar to those that attack man) are found in birds. The former destroy the red blood cells while the latter live in the bone marrow and lymph system. Flagellates (Protozoa with flagella) are also found in the gut. Lice and fleas, amongst insect parasites, and mites and ticks are common on birds and mammals. All are adapted for a life on the outside of their hosts, feeding on the feathers or hair, or sucking blood. The larvae of warbleflies are parasites of economic importance. They are parasitic in the bodies of mammals and cause considerable damage to the skin of cattle (producing warbles), thus seriously reducing the worth of their hides to the leather industry. One wingless fly, *Melophagus* (commonly called the sheep tick), is parasitic on sheep, another on bats. The larvae of tachinid flies are parasitic on the larvae of moths, butterflies, beetles and bugs.

The flatworms (or *Platyhelminthes*) and the roundworms (*Nematoda*) have specialised in parasitism to a greater extent than any other groups. Amongst the flatworms, the flukes and the tapeworms are all parasitic.

eggs must pass to the outside world in order to come into contact with another host. The adults of most internal parasites die before or with their hosts. The eggs pass outside the host and the larvae into which they develop often infect another completely different host species. The beef tapeworm, for example, infects both cattle and man. It is said to have a *two-host life history*. Some parasites infect three different hosts.

One often marvels at the incredible adaptations of many free-living animals: the mimicry of distasteful or dangerous animals by harmless forms, the ability of fishes, cuttle-fish and others to change colour, the storing of fat by animals prior to hibernation: but none better the wonderful refinements of parasites. Many (*e.g.* tapeworms, hookworms) possess hooks or suckers with which they can hang on to the gut lining of their hosts. Fleas and many lice have claws on the ends of their legs with which they can cling to the feathers of birds and the hair of mammals. Gut parasites are able to survive in conditions where there is very little (if any) free oxygen. No doubt the fact that they are surrounded by food and therefore have to expend little energy to obtain it enables them to exist on a minimum of oxygen but even so, these are conditions in which few free-living animals are able to survive. The roundworm *Ascaris*, and tapeworms too, are able to resist the effects of their host's digestive enzymes, and yet at the same time can avail themselves of the digested food. One parasitic barnacle, *Sacculina*, was only recognised as a barnacle when the details of its life history were worked out. Its larva attaches itself to the

weather. Whether in the blood stream, gut, or cells of its host it is surrounded by a ready supply of already digested food (hence the lack or reduction of digestive organs). Its main concern is to take sufficient food for itself without killing its host. Before its host does die of other causes the parasite or its

(left) Sacculina, *a barnacle, parasitic on crabs shown as a yellow mass on the underside of a crab's body; (inset) its larva, typical of barnacles; (right) a drawing showing the extent of the parasites 'roots' (shown in brown) within the crab's body.*

outside of a crab and having spread through the tissues of the crab may appear as a yellow, rounded mass on the underside of a crab's body. It is then little more than a mass of germ cells.

Though the crab may eventually recover from the attack of *Sacculina* usually the parasite reproduces and many young barnacles are then available to infect fresh hosts.

The habit of the female cuckoo of laying its eggs in the nests of meadow pipits, hedge sparrows and reed-warblers is well known. The cuckoo youngsters push the foster-parents' eggs out of the nest and are fed by the foster parents. This is a special form of parasitism.

Parasites are found among plants as well as among animals. A great many fungi live parasitically on other plants or animals. They take all their food from the host and may cause serious diseases, such as potato blight and wheat rust.

Most flowering plants contain chlorophyll and can make their own food, but a few do not contain chlorophyll and send suckers into other plants from which they obtain food. Examples of this type are the dodder, which twines round the stems of clover and other plants, and the toothwort, which obtains food by penetrating the roots of certain trees. Some other plants – the eyebright for example – are partial parasites. They take water from the host roots but make their own food.

A tapeworm and (left) a ripe segment showing the branched uterus full of eggs.

UTERUS

The Balance of Nature

CHAPTER SEVENTEEN

Food Chains

THE basic difference between animals and plants is that the latter can normally manufacture complicated organic food materials from water, carbon dioxide and mineral salts. Animals must obtain ready-made organic food which they can build up into their own bodies.

This picture shows a few of the inter-relationships between plants and animals of land and fresh water.

FIELD MICE ATTACKING BEES' NEST

HUMUS

EARTH WORMS

BURYING-BEETLES WITH DEAD MOLE

OTTER

MOSQUITO LARVAE

PLANKTON

MALARIA PARASITE TRANSMITTED BY MOSQUITOES

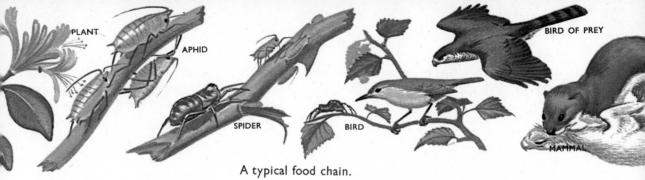

A typical food chain.

Obviously they must depend upon plants for the initial supplies of food materials. The relationship may be a simple one such as a cow eating grass and depending directly upon the plant for food. A slightly more complicated relationship is that of an antelope eating grass and in turn being preyed upon by lions. These relationships are known as *food chains* and they may be made up of many links. All have one thing in common: they all start with a plant as the *primary producer* of food. The first animals to occur in the chain are usually found in large numbers, but successive links are represented by smaller numbers of animals until the major predator in a chain may be represented by a single individual in any given territory. An example of this is found in a field of clover where there will be large numbers of bumble-bees and their underground nests. Field mice, present in smaller numbers, feed on the young bees in the nest and are in turn hunted by hawks. There will probably be only one hawk or family of hawks in the immediate area. The distribution of the hawks depends upon the available food. An area containing five hundred mice obviously cannot support many hawks, as the food supply of the latter would soon be exhausted.

Similar chains are found in the sea. The small planktonic plants – the primary producers – are eaten by planktonic animals which form the food of the shoaling fishes such as herrings. The shoals contain large numbers of fish and are preyed upon by larger fish such as the cod which is not so numerous and does not swim in shoals.

Man can be placed at the head of a great number of chains because he uses a wide variety of natural products for food. Man is, of course, far more common than many of the animals he uses for food, but this is a specialised case and the general rule of decreasing numbers still holds good in other cases.

Parasites must be included in food chains to give a complete picture. The final stage in this case consists of very large numbers of small animals feeding on a single large one. A fish may have hundreds of parasitic round-worms (*nematodes*) inside it. A man ill with malaria has many thousands of protozoan parasites in his blood.

The food chains must not be thought of, however, as simple, straightforward relationships involving only a few animals. All the individual food chains found in a particular environment are linked to each other in some way so that the structure of the animal and plant population of an area remains stable. To take the clover field example again, mice are also preyed upon by owls and by cats. Cats also head a chain leading from dead clover plants via worms and birds, and thus link two chains starting with a clover plant. In theory one can say that the number of

81

cats influences the yield of clover seed via the activities of mice and bees, but so many factors are acting in nature that the effect would probably be balanced out. It is true, however, that severe reduction in the numbers of a common animal will change a lot of things in the environment.

CHAPTER EIGHTEEN

Nature's Dustmen

EVERY living organism, be it plant or animal, depends ultimately upon nitrates and other compounds from the soil. These compounds are vital to the building up of the body's proteins. The supply of nitrates in the world, however, is not inexhaustible and, if they were not returned to the soil when animals die, the supply would soon run out. The series of events by which nitrogen-containing substances are returned to the soil and to other animals is called the *nitrogen cycle*.

The nitrogen cycle is operated by what might be called Nature's Cleansing Department. It employs a large number of workers to dispose of dead bodies and excrement. The efficiency of this 'department' is shown by the

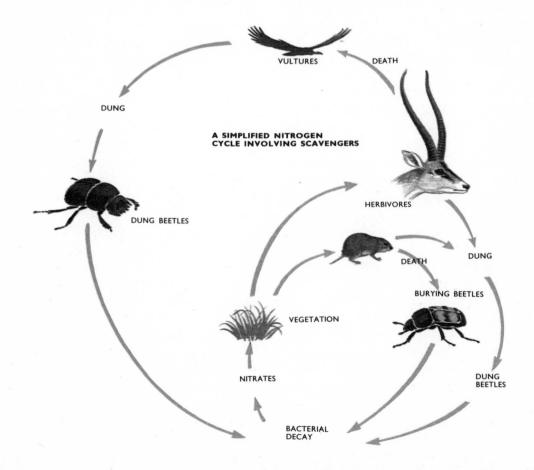

A SIMPLIFIED NITROGEN CYCLE INVOLVING SCAVENGERS

VULTURES

DEATH

DUNG

HERBIVORES

DUNG BEETLES

DEATH

DUNG

BURYING BEETLES

VEGETATION

DUNG BEETLES

NITRATES

BACTERIAL DECAY

fact that one seldom sees dead animals or even skeletons in the countryside.

Bacteria and other micro-organisms play a very important part in the nitrogen cycle and are responsible for the final break down of organic compounds. However, their action is less spectacular than that of various carrion feeders that quickly dispose of dead bodies. Without these carrion feeders the land would be littered with animal bodies in various stages of decay.

Among birds, the best-known of the carrion feeders are the vultures, including the largest living flying bird – the Andean Condor. One group of these birds is distributed over America, and another ranges from the Mediterranean and Africa to India and China. Vultures typically soar high in the sky and can pick out a source of food from very high up. Their sight is quite amazing. Observers have noted that a dead animal quickly attracts several vultures. The soaring birds can probably see each other as well as any food and one swooping bird will attract the attention of others.

A few vultures will rapidly reduce a goat carcass to a mass of skin and bone – ripping the flesh away with their hooked beaks. Their claws are usually weak in comparison to those of other birds of prey which attack living animals. There is even one vulture – the Lammergeyer of the Himalayas and the Middle East – that exists largely on bones and bone marrow. It carries bones up to some height and drops them until they break up.

The scavengers among mammals are the jackals and hyaenas. Jackals are small wolf-like animals that sometimes hunt in packs. They occasionally kill other animals but more often feed on the remains of the lion's kill.

A scarab beetle rolling a ball of dung with its hind legs. An egg laid in the dung develops into a grub that feeds inside the ball (shown cut open). The finished ball is considerably bigger than the beetle itself.

Hyaenas are cowardly animals and will usually attack only small animals such as rats. They feed mostly on carcases and have powerful bone-crushing teeth and jaws. Hyaenas usually go around in groups hunting for carrion.

All that is left after such scavengers is usually a few pieces of skin and bone. These are then attacked by various beetles that find nourishment in such materials. More interesting among the insect scavengers, however, are the various burying beetles and dung-feeders.

Small corpses such as mice and voles rapidly attract the attentions of various sexton beetles. These black, or orange and black, insects have been known to bury a mouse in light soil in a few minutes. The beetles usually work in pairs and bury the corpses by shovelling the soil away from underneath. The head is often broad and aids the legs in the shovelling work. When

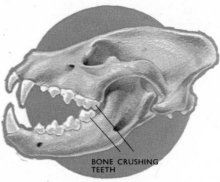

The Striped Hyena and a picture of its skull showing the heavy jaws and the powerful bone-crushing teeth.

buried, the corpse serves as food for the beetles and their larvae. The beetles lay their eggs in the body and the young are already provided with food. Under the soil, the corpse keeps moist and bacterial action can continue more rapidly than it would do at the surface.

In summer, all our meat and fish must be covered to protect it from flies. In the wild, however, these flies do a service by laying their eggs in carcases. The larvae contribute to the breaking

Burying beetles attending to the corpse of a mouse. Several kinds of beetle engage in this work. In sandy soil, the corpse is rapidly buried.

down of the material and its eventual return to the soil.

Almost before the dung of cattle and other animals has cooled it is visited by flies and beetles. They feed there and lay their eggs. The grubs rapidly absorb the putrefying material leaving only a collection of dried plant remains – valuable food for some beetles.

Beetles of the scarab family are well known buriers of animal dung. The once-sacred scarab of Egypt collects dung and rolls it into a ball and then rolls the ball to some suitable place for burial. Some scarabs feed on the dung themselves while others may use it to lay eggs in. The Dor-Beetle a relative of the scarab, tunnels underneath cow dung and fills the ends of the tunnels with dung before laying its eggs there.

The value of these scavengers and the myriads of insects and other organisms that break down plant and animal remains is enormous. The fact that bacteria and other micro-organisms can reduce refuse to harmless, even useful material, has only recently been used by Man in composting plants. This is an attempt by Man to avoid wastage and to return material to the soil as is done by Nature's own dustmen.

Animal Behaviour

CHAPTER NINETEEN

Learning and Instinct

THE thrush is not taught to build its nest nor the garden spider to spin its web. These are instincts – actions which are inborn and do not have to be learned.

Instincts are common in the animal kingdom, particularly amongst the lower orders of life. They account for much of animal behaviour – courtship displays, protective care of the young, migratory drives and reaction to dangers. The pattern of behaviour begins usually after a stimulus to one or more of the sense organs. Such a stimulus is called a *releaser*. A loud noise – and instinctively, animals take evasive action, fleeing or crouching motionless to the ground. Instincts like nest-building and web and cocoon spinning are perfect from the start. Caterpillars of different species of moth spin their own types of cocoon once only in their lives – but they do it perfectly. Young birds reared in isolation away from parents nevertheless build exactly similar nests even down to the material

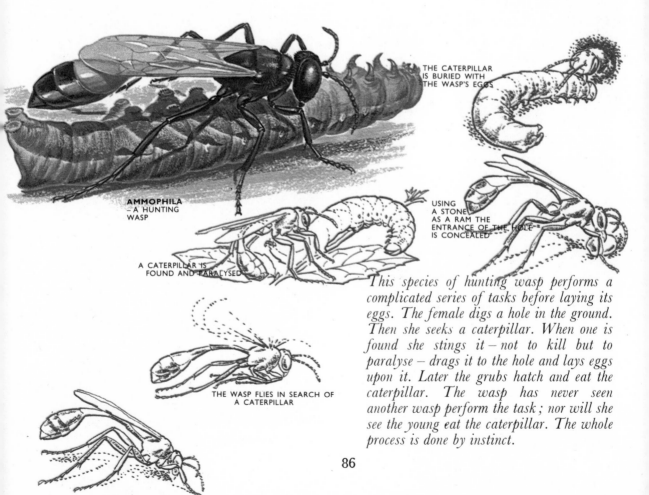

THE CATERPILLAR IS BURIED WITH THE WASP'S EGGS

AMMOPHILA
—A HUNTING
WASP

USING
A STONE
AS A RAM THE
ENTRANCE OF THE HOLE
IS CONCEALED

A CATERPILLAR IS
FOUND AND PARALYSED

THE WASP FLIES IN SEARCH OF
A CATERPILLAR

A HOLE IS DUG

This species of hunting wasp performs a complicated series of tasks before laying its eggs. The female digs a hole in the ground. Then she seeks a caterpillar. When one is found she stings it – not to kill but to paralyse – drags it to the hole and lays eggs upon it. Later the grubs hatch and eat the caterpillar. The wasp has never seen another wasp perform the task; nor will she see the young eat the caterpillar. The whole process is done by instinct.

used. Other instincts like Man's instinct to walk take time and practice to become perfect.

Each species of animal has its own different range and type of instinct. All members of a species will usually behave in much the same way to a stimulus. Instincts are just as much a part of an animal as the structures which identify its body.

Instincts are purposeful. Although carried out without any learning or reason, they fulfil a definite and usually valuable function. Some are simple enough. A mole bites off the heads of worms it wishes to store for food. The body of the worm remains alive, but devoid of its head, it cannot burrow and escape. More complicated are the engineering feats of the beaver. The beaver fells trees, transports them along specially constructed canals and builds them into dams.

A variety of instinctive behaviour is associated with courtship in different species. The bold parading of pheasant and turkey cocks are common examples. Male redstarts hold a singing contest, ringed plovers demonstrate their powers of flight, while deer and many other animals engage in contests of strength.

More amazing are certain impulsive instincts to emigrate from a region. When their populations become overcrowded in Norway, hundreds of thousands of *lemmings*, vole-like rodents, begin a colossal mass migration from their homes. Unless a new unoccupied territory is reached the migration continues. The death rate is enormous for the fleeing lemmings are easy prey; many more drown in the rivers and seas they encounter. Similar emigrations have been observed in the Springbok of South Africa. Less drastic are the seasonal migrations of birds and animals. Regular passages are made from areas where reproduction takes place to regions in which winter is **spent.**

Defensive mechanisms are instinctive. They do not have to be learned. The porcupine erects its quills and rattles them when danger threatens. Cats spit and ruffle their fur; some animals such as the octopus produce frightening colours.

The Opossum has a curious defence mechanism. It pretends to be dead. It becomes limp, its eyes close, its heart slows down. When danger is past the creature quickly revives.

The caterpillar of the puss-moth, when disturbed, withdraws its head under its thorax. The thorax, as a result, swells and displays two prominent eye-like lumps. In addition, a pair of whiplashes (modified prolegs) beat the air over the caterpillar.

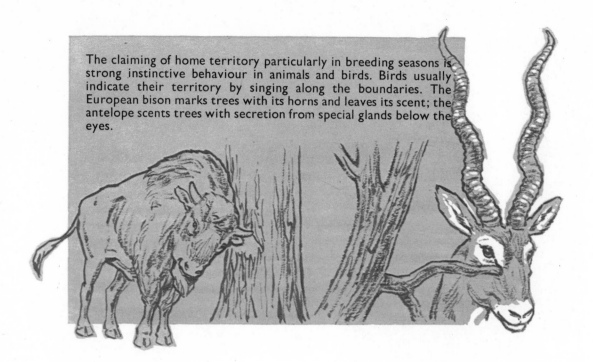

The claiming of home territory particularly in breeding seasons is strong instinctive behaviour in animals and birds. Birds usually indicate their territory by singing along the boundaries. The European bison marks trees with its horns and leaves its scent; the antelope scents trees with secretion from special glands below the eyes.

Animals which live in communities tend to copy the actions of one another. This instinct is called *mimesis* (mime-EE-sis). Man is no exception to this instinct; if one person yawns others follow suit. The value of all examples of mimesis is not clear. But undoubtedly the copying of others has some survival value. If one animal spots danger and flees, those following also avoid trouble.

Self preservation is a universal instinct in the animal kingdom. Yet when rearing young, the instinct to protect the offspring is often even stronger. Many mammals and birds will stand and fight an aggressor when normally they would have fled. Ground-nesting birds such as the skylark may put on a decoy display. When an aggressor appears, near the nest, the parent bird attracts attention to itself by screeching and flapping its wings.

Because there is no forethought or reasoning behind instincts, their function sometimes becomes impaired. The male penguin, for instance, incu-

The instinct to walk is not present in young babies. The nerve cells responsible for walking are not yet fully developed. The walking instinct needs time before it becomes perfect. Riding a bicycle or driving a car is not instinctive. The necessary muscular co-ordination has to be learned by practice.

Some instincts are always present in an animal – defensive attitudes and defensive colour changes for instance. Other instincts appear only at certain times. Such periodic occurrences of instinct are often due to the action of *hormones* – chemical substances secreted by glands inside the body. The hormones pass into the blood stream and so reach the brain. Marked changes in animal behaviour can often be brought about by upsetting the hormone balance.

The activity of the hormone does not itself directly cause a piece of behaviour. It makes possible one or a whole series of instinctive actions when certain outside signals are received from the outside world. At breeding periods for instance, a male bird may display to a female of the same species whereas the appearance of another male causes aggressive behaviour.

Sometimes instinctive drives may be so powerful that they produce behaviour without the usual outside stimulus. In the absence of a mate, captive birds and animals may display to their keepers instead.

Instincts are obviously of great value to animals. They provide a method of survival and a method of successfully breeding and rearing offspring. They have been built up over the ages by the process of natural selection. The individuals performing certain types of behaviour will survive to transmit them to their young.

bates the egg laid by the female, by supporting it on its foot. If no egg becomes available the penguin will obey its instinct by substituting a round stone. Birds feed their young because the sight of gaping mouths is the releaser to supply food. It does not matter whether it is their own young or not – food is pushed into any gaping mouth. Blackbirds have been known to feed the hungry young of Great Tits; foster-parents feed the young cuckoo hatched in their nest without any hesitation.

Instinctive behaviour with apparently the least purpose, is found in animals taken away from their natural environments. Dogs still bury bones despite regular feeding; they even may turn around a few times before settling down in their baskets – as though flattening grass into a good bed.

Learning

Instincts regulate the lives of animals like pieces of machinery. An outside action takes place, this provides a stimulus and a fixed pattern of behaviour takes place. Animals which rely largely upon instincts – nearly all except some of the mammals and birds – lack *personality*. They all behave in much the same way as other members of their species.

Escape from this internal machine is to some extent possible – by a process of *learning*. Learning has the effect of modifying the instinct. Actions no longer take place blindly but are conditioned by past experiences. Two simple types of learning are *habituation* and *association*. In habituation, the initial instinct is lost. Though the old stimulus occurs there is no reaction to it. Domestic animals for instance no longer flee from Man. Association (or conditioning) takes place when the original stimulus is replaced by another. Domestic animals may no longer associate Man with danger but instead with food or comfort.

Association is the method by which animals remember. An encounter leading to an unpleasant experience is avoided at a future date. An encounter which ended in a reward will be repeated. In this manner animals can be trained.

The ability to 'remember' exists to some degree in even simple animals

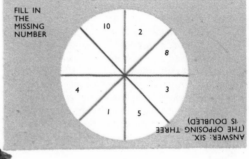

This chimpanzee shows signs of insight-learning. Without previously encountering this situation, it uses a bamboo stick to reach out and drag bananas into its cage. Human beings can likewise solve problems which they have never encountered before, only to a much greater degree.

FILL IN THE MISSING NUMBER

10   2
        8
4   3
  1   5

ANSWER: SIX, (THE OPPOSING THREE IS DOUBLED)

such as snails and worms. By experience with mild electric shocks they learn to avoid making journeys which will bring them in contact with the shock. Bees and wasps certainly have the ability to learn. They soon recognize the landmarks surrounding their nests or hives and are able to move about without losing their way.

By trial-and-error an animal builds up solutions to a number of problems.

A dog attempting to reach food on the other side of a fence may come across a hole in the fence. He remembers the hole on future occasions and when presented with a different fence may again search for an outlet. In this way dogs appear to reason though all they are doing in fact is remembering similar past situations.

Man has not only the ability to learn by trial-and-error but has developed a

A chick inside an egg shell instinctively pecks its way out into the world. Without this instinct the chick would suffocate inside the egg. What can be eaten and what cannot, is learned. At first, the chick pecks at anything – pebbles and wood. By association it learns what objects make good food.

further type of learning. This is *insight-learning* – the ability to think out a situation before taking any action. A completely new problem never encountered before is overcome by re-organizing all previous experiences. A solution is found not by the long and troublesome method of trial-and-error. Nor is there a similar problem of the past to remember. The brain simply reasons its way forward from a number of general observations and experiences.

Monkeys have been found to possess something of this ability. They have obtained food placed out of reach by piling up boxes one on top of the other and they have used sticks to reach food outside of their cages. These are truly reasoned actions for they could never have encountered exactly similar problems in the wild. Dogs, rats and a few other mammals also have some reasoning ability, though usually they only solve a problem of which they have had past experience. The enormous development of insight-learning has helped Man to master the world around him.

CHAPTER TWENTY

Hibernation – The Winter Sleep

IN cold and temperate regions, many animals disappear at the beginning of winter. They may disappear because they cannot withstand the cold, or because they are unable to obtain food during the cold season. Many birds migrate to warmer lands but among other animals, *hibernation* is common. This is a state of inactivity or deep sleep during which the body processes slow down almost to a stop. The body temperature, even in mammals, falls to within a degree or two of that of their immediate surroundings. A similar sort of inactivity, called *aestivation*, is common in some desert-living and pond-living creatures, which burrow down into the ground and thereby avoid hot and dry conditions.

Hibernation in Cold-blooded Animals

During the short polar summers, the pools abound with life. Millions of tiny one-celled animals seem to appear from nowhere. In fact, they have passed the long cold winter in tiny, hard-walled *cysts*. When the cold weather sets in, the animals form the protective coat and remain within it, almost lifeless. The same is true for nematode worms and other small creatures. Their tiny cysts have been collected from frozen soil, dried ponds and other highly unfavourable places. They seem quite lifeless, yet when given good conditions they spring to life. The almost lifeless state is called *anabiosis* (=without life).

Although many aquatic animals remain active below the covering of ice, their land-living relatives frequently hibernate. The common garden snails cover the openings of their shells with a slime containing calcium phosphate that hardens into a tough protective covering. So protected, they pass the winter amid rotting vegeta-

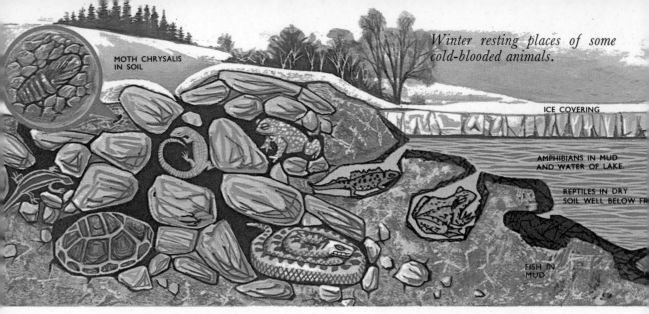

MOTH CHRYSALIS IN SOIL

Winter resting places of some cold-blooded animals.

ICE COVERING

AMPHIBIANS IN MUD AND WATER OF LAKE.

REPTILES IN DRY SOIL WELL BELOW FR

FISH IN MUD

tion or under logs and stones.

Insects may pass the winter in any of the four life-stages. Probably, the majority over-winter as eggs which are very resistant to cold and to drying. The eggs of many species will not hatch until they have been subjected to a period of cold. This enforced rest is called a *diapause* and is also found in the grubs and pupae. Even when kept in the warm, the insects will go into a state of inactivity for a while. Hibernating caterpillars may be found among the dead leaves in ditches and hedgerows and the chrysalids (pupae) of many moths can be dug up from the soil. The butterflies that come out

The African Lungfish aestivates deep in the mud. It surrounds itself with mucus to keep moist and breathes through a small opening in the mucus. The narrow opening prevents much loss of water and the fish survives until the rains return.

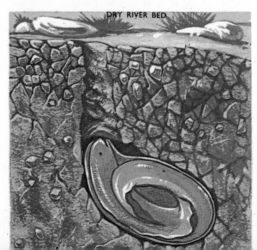

DRY RIVER BED

with the first spring sunshine have all over-wintered as adults, secure in some outhouse or attic.

Fishes rarely hibernate although some species become lethargic in cold weather and may remain motionless, partly buried in the mud. Lung-fishes, however, aestivate during the dry period when their pools often dry up. They burrow down into the mud and form a resting chamber from which little moisture escapes.

Amphibians and reptiles are well-known hibernators. Frogs, tortoises, snakes and lizards all bury themselves away from the effect of frost. They often huddle together and this habit undoubtedly helps to keep their temperature a degree or two above that of the surroundings. Some of these animals seem able to expel water from their tissues. This makes the remaining fluids more concentrated and lowers their freezing point. The animals can then endure temperatures below 0°C without becoming frozen solid.

Hibernation in Warm-blooded Animals

True hibernation is not known among birds although some become drowsy during cold weather. Night-

92

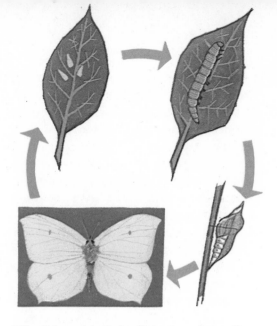

The life-cycle of the Brimstone butterfly – one that hibernates as an adult. Many other insects pass the winter as eggs, grubs, or pupae.

jars are insect-eating birds. European ones migrate to South Africa in winter. However, the Poor-will, an American nightjar, has recently been found to pass the winter in a state of semi-hibernation. The temperature of these sleeping birds is about 65°F instead of the normal 100° of the active bird. Many mammals, too, hide away and remain drowsy during the winter months. Bears, badgers, tree squirrels and others go to sleep for varying periods of time, but they wake periodically and may feed on stored food. Their temperature does not drop more than a few degrees below normal, however. True hibernation, where the body temperature falls almost to that of the surroundings, is found in only a few groups of mammals. The egg-laying monotremes and some of the opossums are known to hibernate in cold winters. Bats of temperate and cold climates hibernate because they cannot catch insects in winter. Bats are peculiar, however, in that their temperature drops considerably every

time they sleep, even in the summer-time. In this torpid condition they use less energy and they can be more active when they are awake.

Some insect-eating mammals – notably the hedgehog – and many rodents (e.g. dormice, ground-squirrels and hamsters) also go into a deep winter sleep. Even so, these hibernators often wake up and may feed on stored food. Ground squirrels certainly do this. It seems that periodic waking is essential for getting rid of accumulated waste.

Before they go into hibernation, animals often put on weight, in the form of fatty deposits. This extra material is drawn upon during the winter sleep. Others store nuts and other food on which to draw when they wake at intervals. It is not known what stimulus causes these preparations, nor are the physiological processes of hibernation fully understood. Temperature and lack of food probably contribute to the onset of hibernation and the length of the day may possibly be concerned. There must also be some internal control because close relatives of hibernating animals often remain active in the cold season.

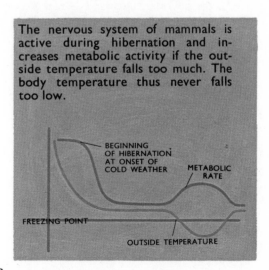

The nervous system of mammals is active during hibernation and increases metabolic activity if the outside temperature falls too much. The body temperature thus never falls too low.

BEGINNING OF HIBERNATION AT ONSET OF COLD WEATHER

METABOLIC RATE

FREEZING POINT

OUTSIDE TEMPERATURE

At the start of hibernation the temperature-regulating mechanism is disturbed and the body temperature falls. The regulating mechanism may fail in response to prolonged cold. A short cold spell will not necessarily lead to hibernation. As the body temperature falls, the other activities slow down. Less oxygen is used, less food material is used, breathing slows down and the heart-beat rate also slows down. The animal is then in a deep sleep. Its metabolic rate (the rate at which the body processes go on) is less than a thirtieth (even as low as one hundredth) of that of the active animal. These changes are probably the result of hormone action. All the while, however, the nervous system is in control. If the outside temperature drops too much, the heart-beat quickens and the body temperature increases to maintain life.

The end of hibernation is brought about by some stimulus such as the temperature rise in the surroundings and is probably controlled by the nervous system. The body processes increase their rate and shivering often occurs – producing more heat. In the hamster, an hour or two is all that is necessary for the animal to wake and regain its normal temperature. Bats possibly need an even shorter time. During the waking process a great deal of energy is used and so, although a hibernating animal does wake periodically, too frequent disturbances can be fatal. An animal will quickly use up its supplies of fat and, unless it has a store of food on which to draw, it will soon perish.

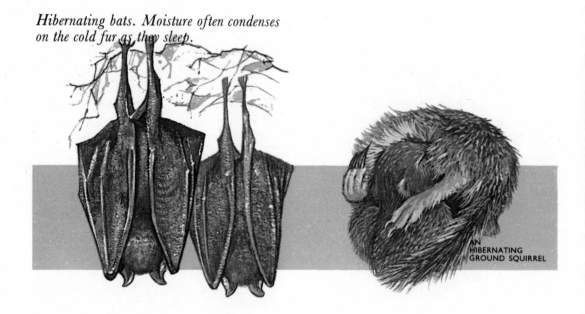

Hibernating bats. Moisture often condenses on the cold fur as they sleep.

AN HIBERNATING GROUND SQUIRREL

CHAPTER TWENTY-ONE

Migration and Emigration

MANY shifts of animal populations are caused by certain behaviour patterns of the animals themselves. There is *migration* – a fairly regular to-and-fro movement from one area to another and back again; and there is *emigration*, in contrast, a sudden random movement of animals – the animals do not return to their original territory.

Migration

The swallow winters in tropical and sub-tropical climates. In summer it flies northwards into temperate zones. Here reproduction takes place. The following winter the bird returns to the tropics. The advantages of the migration are easy to see. Winter cold, in the north, with accompanying shortage of food is avoided. So are the torrid summers of the tropics.

Even more vital are the migrations of amphibians. Frogs, toads and newts live most of their lives on land, but to

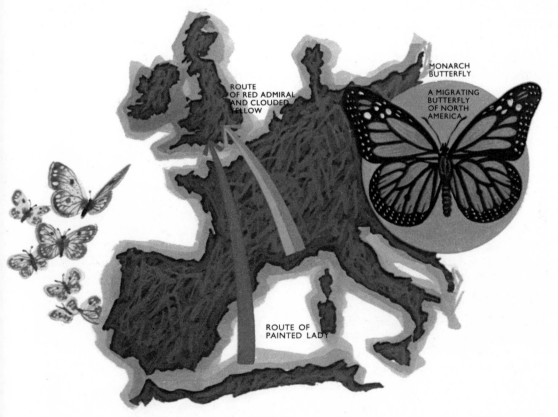

ROUTE OF RED ADMIRAL AND CLOUDED YELLOW

MONARCH BUTTERFLY

A MIGRATING BUTTERFLY OF NORTH AMERICA

ROUTE OF PAINTED LADY

Butterflies migrate from North Africa as well as birds. Routes are shown of the Painted Lady, Red Admiral and Clouded Yellow. The reason for the migration is not clear. Nor is the method by which the butterflies navigate. Inset: Monarch butterfly, a well-known migrating butterfly of North America.

Migratory and emigratory behaviour is instinctive. No conscious thought is involved. The action is entirely automatic. In the higher animals the pattern of behaviour is induced by changes in the hormonal system, particularly by influence of the pituitary gland. Some outside stimulation or stimulations are normally required to affect the hormonal system. Increasing or decreasing length of day may be important, together with associated climatic variations. Vertical migrations in planktonic animals may be directly caused by differences in light intensity, temperature and salinity.

The stimulus for emigration seems to be the overcrowding of a species with the consequent shortage of food and space, and the appearance of social stresses and abnormalities of behaviour.

breed, they must return to water. Consequently, each spring, a migration takes place from surrounding areas to local pools and rivers. The distance of the migration, in contrast to that covered by the swallow, is often very small.

Migrations are especially common amongst creatures living in polar regions, or on high mountainous slopes. The harsh winters are avoided by movement into more sheltered places. The caribou, spending the summer wandering in the tundra, with the onset of winter move into the taiga – the northern coniferous forests. Mountain sheep, goats and chamois vacate the rocky upper slopes and move to lower levels. The greatest traveller of all is the arctic tern. This bird flies seasonally from arctic to antarctic regions – a distance of twenty odd thousand miles.

Less commonly known migrants are some hermit crabs which each year travel to the sea to breed and then return to land. Fishes are also great migrants; cod seasonally move to the north-west Atlantic to spawn; salmon and sturgeon pass from the sea into freshwater rivers, while the European eel may migrate 3,000 miles from Europe to the Sargasso sea to spawn.

Migrations are not necessarily seasonal. Some planktonic animals drifting in surface waters have a diurnal rhythm – a migration which takes place once every 24 hours. The organisms do not move horizontally. Instead they move from one level of water to another. The reason is rather obscure, for the migration takes place in different species at different times. Some creatures, for instance, sink during the day, rising at night; others the reverse. A possible long-term advantage is the continued change of feeding ground. One hundred feet down, the water is slow-moving compared with the faster-moving surface waters. On returning to the surface the organism has effectively changed its surroundings – for fresh surface water has replaced the surface water in which the organism was originally swimming.

Euphasia of the Antarctic retains its geographical position by migration each 24 hours. During the night these animals drift northwards in the current of cold water. Then they sink 600 feet and are moved by a current of warm water replacing the cold water.

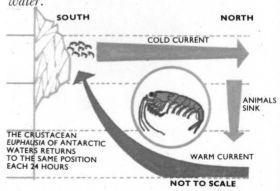

SOUTH   NORTH

COLD CURRENT

ANIMALS SINK

THE CRUSTACEAN
EUPHAUSIA OF ANTARCTIC
WATERS RETURNS
TO THE SAME POSITION
EACH 24 HOURS

WARM CURRENT

NOT TO SCALE

S. AMERICAN ALLIGATOR MIGRATES TO MAIN RIVERS WHEN TRIBUTARIES DRY UP

FROGS RETURN TO WATER FOR BREEDING

SOME BATS MIGRATE IN SEARCH OF FOODS

SEALS CONGREGATE FOR BREEDING

All sorts of animals migrate. Migration may lead to an increase in food and ensures a species is spread over, and is exploring as large an area as possible. Migration alternatively may bring about congregation for breeding purposes, of animals which are by habit scattered over a wide area.

Emigration

In contrast, *emigration* by animals are population movements *without return*. Also called *irruptions*, they are intricately related to the size of the population of a species. A build-up in numbers producing overcrowding seems responsible for the outward drive. The lemmings of the arctic are famous for their periodic emigrations. Arctic voles and snow-shoe rabbits behave similarly, and away from polar regions so do some antelopes (such as the springbok) and some birds such as the waxwing. Usually emigrating creatures are doomed. Their headlong flight is accompanied by hysteria – an almost complete loss of self-preservative instincts. Apparently without fear, they are easy prey for following predators. Coming to rivers, seas or lakes, they move heedlessly on usually to self-destruction. But some emigrations in the past have met with spectacular success. The brown rat, now common in Europe, was unknown there before 1773. Then a huge invasion took place from the east. Descriptions of the swarms of rats swimming the great European rivers survive. Millions were drowned but some lived to continue the march. Soon the whole of Europe was occupied. The brown rats' successful entry into Europe can be closely compared with the 'suicidal' runs of lemmings today. The rats' invasion probably met with little competition

BEES SWARMING

The emigration of the brown rat at the end of the 18th century widely dispersed the species all over Europe. Though millions drowned in swimming the great rivers separating Asia from Europe, many survived, to breed. Right: a swarm of bees represents emigration in the insect world. Overcrowding of a hive leads to a division of the colony.

97

The vertical migration of the majority of plankton seems to ensure a change in surroundings. During each 24 hours, animals sink. When they return, currents have completely 'changed' the water with its food supplies.

from other creatures. Alternatively, the invasion coincided with slight climatic changes making the new territories more acceptable to the brown rat.

Thus emigrations are not by nature doomed from the start. Under certain conditions they mean, not mass destruction, but the colonization of new territories; the species becomes dispersed over wider areas. Even when emigrations do end in disaster, the species is favoured as a whole, for those few that do not migrate will become better fed and more healthy and more likely to breed successfully.

Emigrations are not confined to the more advanced vertebrate animals. Similar movements are found in bees (swarming), locusts, dragonflies, ants, butterflies and termites.

Nomadism

Nomadism is a permanently wandering mode of living found almost exclusively amongst the higher animals. Lower animals nearly all have a strong 'homing instinct' and though they do move around, they invariably return to a permanent place of 'residence'. Nomadism is found particularly in mammals of desert regions or sparse plains. The vegetation being insufficient to provide enough food for a permanent population, the animals are forced to constantly change their feeding grounds. Nomadism is also found amongst amphibians and reptiles. Amongst birds it is rare; birds can travel such immense distances that, though ranging over vast territories, nevertheless they can easily reach their homes.

CHAPTER TWENTY-TWO

Bird Migration

FOR over two thousand years man has been intrigued by the fact that some birds stay in the same place all the year round, whilst others disappear in late summer or early autumn and reappear in the spring. There are other birds that do the reverse of this: they come to us in the autumn and leave us in the spring. In time various explanations were put forward to account for this. Some of these, by our standards, were rather stupid, yet they were firmly believed. Cuckoos were supposed to turn into sparrowhawks for the winter, and swallows were said to spend the winter at the bottom of lakes.

It was not until the middle of the eighteenth century that the second of these was disproved, when a German naturalist, Johann Fritsch, tied pieces of dyed thread on the legs of swallows. Then, when they returned to the same nesting site the following year, he noted that the threads were still there and the dye had not been washed out.

During the eighteenth century, also, naturalists began comparing notes. As a result they realized that many birds regularly spend the winter in one place and the summer in another. Interest grew and many new methods of

Checking the ring on a Goldfinch. This hold is quite harmless for the bird. (Inset) The ringing pliers *that painlessly secure rings to all sizes of bird.*

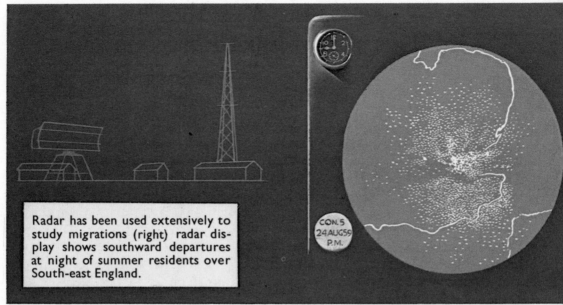

Radar has been used extensively to study migrations (right) radar display shows southward departures at night of summer residents over South-east England.

Courtesy: Marconi's Wireless Telegraph Co. Ltd.

observation were devised. As more and more lighthouses were built and lightships constructed, it was noticed that birds often flew into the lamps. William Eagle Clark of the Royal Scottish Museum spent many weeks on lighthouses and lightships taking note and, later, many other observers joined in. Bird observatories, like the famous one at Heligoland, were founded.

In 1891, Christian C. Mortensen, in Denmark, began fixing thin pieces of zinc to the feet of birds, the forerunners of the aluminium bird rings in use today. Over ten million birds have since been ringed in Germany, North America and Britain alone. The birds are trapped harmlessly and light rings are fitted to the leg. The ring bears a number and an address, and when the bird is caught again, the ring tells where it came from, and when and where the bird was ringed.

The Pattern of Migration

All the information obtained in this way has been patiently plotted until now we have the picture of a vast general post taking place twice yearly. Some birds fly north to south, others east to west, and back again. Yet others live among the coniferous forest on the slopes of mountains during the summer, flying down to low-lying areas as the weather gets more severe in the winter.

Then there are those birds that make incredibly long journeys. European swallows spend the summer in Europe and the winter in South Africa, some reaching the Cape of Good Hope, a distance of about five thousand miles. Tree swallows gather

GOLDEN PLOVER

in huge flocks to migrate in the autumn. From the northern half of the United States and Canada they fly south to Mexico and the regions bordering the Gulf of Mexico.

The longest journey is made by the Arctic tern. It nests in the summer in the Arctic and then flies to the Antarctic for the winter (which is the southern summer), a journey of eleven thousand miles each way.

Another of the more remarkable migrations is that of the Golden Plover, which flies from Alaska to the Hawaiian Islands, a journey of two thousand miles without landfall.

Flyways

The flyways or migration routes are not always in a straight line, but tend to follow well-defined routes often along coastlines (during the daytime, not at night), through valleys or over mountain ranges. In Europe, migrating birds follow mainly three routes that give the shortest sea crossings: through France and across the Iberian Peninsula and the Straits of Gibraltar to Africa, through Italy or across the Balkans, through Turkey and Asia Minor to Egypt. Often, however, migrations are made over the sea.

How High do Migrating Birds Fly?

On the whole, birds do not fly high on migration, only a few hundred feet. It is not unusual to hear flocks of migrating birds flying overhead by night, even in big cities. Sometimes the birds fly very low, particularly over the sea and when there is a head-wind. Others fly high to avoid the weather. Geese have been seen migrating at a height of twenty-six thousand feet.

Why and How do Birds Migrate?

There have been many theories about why birds migrate and how they find their way. One suggestion was that they use the Earth's magnetism to guide them. Another was that they have some kind of racial memory, so that each generation always follows the same route. Yet another theory was that the older birds act as guides, but then we find that young cuckoos, who never see their parents, fly south a month after the old cuckoos have departed.

One of the most remarkable features of migration is the way a bird, such as a swift or swallow, will travel thousands of miles and return to the same nesting site as it used the year before. One particular swift was known to have made the journey from Britain to Africa every year without fail for four years in succession.

There are obvious advantages and

ARCTIC TERN

GREENLAND WHEATEAR

SWALLOW

disadvantages in migration. For birds that live in high latitudes, the main advantage appears to be the greatly increased range that they obtain. During the summer they are able to inhabit regions that are unsuitable in the winter, either because of cold or lack of food. The fact that they fly north for the summer months means, of course, that they have to fly south with the onset of winter to avoid the unsuitable conditions. But they do inhabit the more northerly latitudes when conditions there are at their best. A bird such as the Arctic tern has the best of both worlds, for it enjoys the near continuous light of both the Arctic and Antarctic summers.

Migration ensures that each bird species is spread over, and is exploring, as large an area as possible. This may well increase the chances of their meeting unfavourable conditions, but the chance of discovering new, favourable habitats is also there. The Greenland Wheatear has certainly increased its range northwards in recent times. This has been linked with the higher temperatures that prevail in these latitudes at the present time.

Since 1945 radar has been used extensively to study migrations. In the same way that radio waves are reflected from an aircraft or a ship, they are reflected from birds. In fact, during the Second World War, 'blips' on radar screens which were thought to represent aircraft or ships at different times turned out to be birds. The use of radar has revealed such information as how high birds fly, how fast they fly, and how bad weather affects their migrations.

Observers plotting the migration of birds are hampered by the narrow fields of vision and hearing within which they can work. The advantage of plotting bird migration with radar screens lies in the broader view it can take. For example, in 1953 it was shown that out of a group of birds migrating in a broad front across a coastline, a few may turn after crossing the coast and move parallel to it. An observer stationed at one point may pick these up and report a heavy coastwise migration and be quite unaware that the main movement is at right angles to their path.

New knowledge has also come to light in other ways. A German scientist, Dr. G. Kramer, carried out experiments which showed that birds find their way by the sun. Later, it was found that when birds were kept inside a dome with stars painted on its inner surface they changed their position as the ceiling, and therefore the stars, was rotated. It is fairly certain that birds have an 'internal chronometer', that they can note the differing positions of the sun at different times, and that, using a time-sense, they can navigate by the sun during the daytime or by the stars at night.

This would explain why migrating birds lose themselves in foggy and cloudy weather (also such conditions temporarily postpone long migrations). Another reason for this loss of direction could be that they also use landmarks to some extent. A swallow flying to Europe from Africa would set course by the sun and the stars, and these would guide it on its way across Africa and Europe. When it was nearing its destination it would doubtless take note of landmarks to find the particular barn or stable in which it nested last year.

The ability of birds to 'home' is

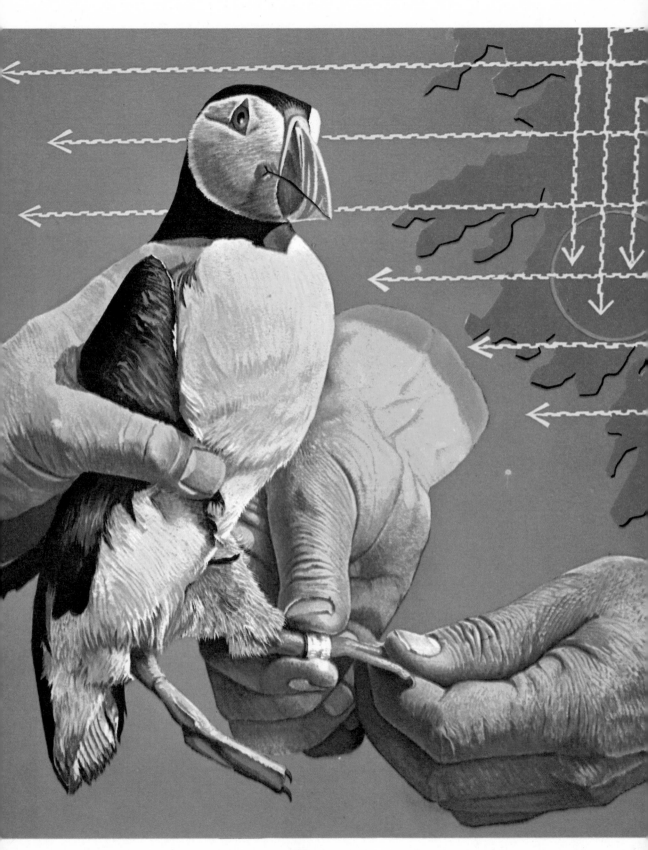

remarkable. A bird, such as a pigeon, can be trained to home from considerable distances. This is done by releasing the pigeon further and further away from its roost. One pigeon found its way home when it was released a thousand miles away. Untrained pigeons do not find their way home as consistently as trained pigeons – strong evidence as to the importance of landmarks near the nesting site.

Then we have the surprising story of the scientists in South Georgia, in the Antarctic, who ringed penguins on their nests, and carefully mapped the positions of the nests. Later, the penguins migrated hundreds of miles by swimming or sliding on their bellies over the ice. The next year they returned to the nesting area, but the winter had lingered and practically the whole of South Georgia was covered with snow, obliterating the landmarks. The penguins began to collect stones from the beach, with which to make their nests as usual, but they deposited these on top of the snow. When the snow melted, the stones began to drop until finally they rested on the ground – in exactly the same places that their nests had been built the year before!

Such achievements cannot be explained at present, but one thing is certain, the homing abilities of birds are far beyond those of man.

CHAPTER TWENTY-THREE

Colour in the Animal World

MAN'S wide range of colour vision is shared only by the other primates – the apes and monkeys. Most, if not all, other mammals are believed to see only black and white and various shades of grey. The bullfighter's cape would work equally well were it blue or green, for it is the movement of the cape and not its colour that enrages the animal. Many other animals, however, do see colour, although their range is generally less than that of Man. Birds, many insects and fishes see colours and it is significant that these animals are frequently brightly coloured. Whether they have good colour vision or not, colour plays a big part in the life of animals.

Colour For Concealment

Unless they have a special defence or escape mechanism, animals must conceal themselves from their enemies. One way is to merge with the colour of the surroundings. Where such resemblance is useful, natural selection has produced beautifully adapted animals. Various moths and leaf insects are good examples. The mainly brown grazing animals merge with the plains where they feed – especially when one remembers that their enemies – lions and the like – see only in shades of grey. This general colour resemblance, however, is only part of the answer. A solid body will tend to

Diagram to show how countershading helps to conceal animals. The top animal is plain-coloured and shadows appear underneath. The shadows are countered by the pale underside of the bottom animal and, at a distance, it disappears.

How Colour is Produced

Colour in the living world is produced in two main ways. *Pigments* are important and are found in all types of animals. The molecules of pigments absorb light of particular wavelengths and reflect or transmit the unabsorbed wavelengths, so producing the colour. Pigments are often by-products of metabolic processes and are deposited at various points in the body.

Melanins – the common black and brown pigments are deposited in the outer layers of the skin including the hair. Many pigments are lodged in granules of fat and may disappear upon death – the brilliant colours of some dragonflies are of this type.

Structural colours depend on the arrangement of molecules and larger particles in the body. Thin layers laid upon each other cause interference in the light rays and break up the white light. Iridescence results with many blue and purple sheens, although white can also be produced by scattering of light rays.

stand out in relief against the background of shading effects.

A great many animals have darker colours on the top surface than underneath. This feature is called *counter-shading* and was first explained by a biologist called Thayer. In Nature, the light usually comes from above

and there is shadow below. This effect is countered by the coloration of the body and the result is that all shadows disappear and the animal merges as a flat shape into the background. Counter-shading is prominent among the grazing mammals where it is produced by a gradation of colour or by

Not all animals see an object in the same colours. The pictures show how a bunch of flowers will appear to Man (A), a dog (B), and many birds and fishes (C).

Above: The Red Underwing moth rests on tree trunks. When disturbed, it flies off with a flash of the red hind wing and quickly settles again. The red flash deceives the enemy. Below: Warning coloration of the Cinnabar moth and its caterpillar, both of which are unpleasant to taste.

The larva of the Eyed hawk moth normally hangs upside down and shading effects partly conceal it. If put the other way up (top), it stands out in relief.

patterns that change lower down the body. The zebra's stripes and the giraffe's pattern for instance produce counter-shading when seen at a distance. These patterns are also *disruptive.*

Disruptive colouring is another very important feature of animal life. Contrasting colours and patterns break up the outline of the body and draw attention away from the whole shape. Although an animal with disruptive coloration may look obvious close to or out of its natural surroundings, against a natural background it may completely disappear. Fishes, snakes and many ground-nesting birds make use of this type of coloration.

Warning Coloration

Many animals – especially insects – that are poisonous or distasteful are brightly coloured. Wasps, Cinnabar moths and caterpillars are good examples. Alfred Russel Wallace was the first naturalist to put forward the warning coloration theory. It is that the bold yellow or red and black pattern will quickly be learnt by birds and other predators and will be associated with unpleasant taste. The insects will then be left alone. In fact,

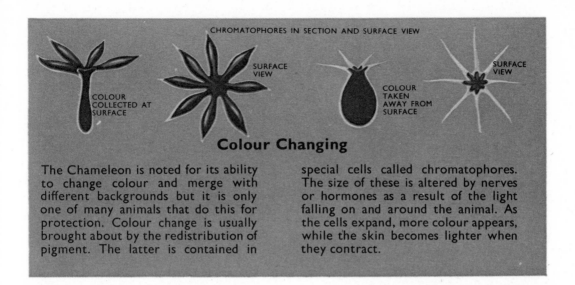

CHROMATOPHORES IN SECTION AND SURFACE VIEW

COLOUR COLLECTED AT SURFACE

SURFACE VIEW

COLOUR TAKEN AWAY FROM SURFACE

SURFACE VIEW

Colour Changing

The Chameleon is noted for its ability to change colour and merge with different backgrounds but it is only one of many animals that do this for protection. Colour change is usually brought about by the redistribution of pigment. The latter is contained in special cells called chromatophores. The size of these is altered by nerves or hormones as a result of the light falling on and around the animal. As the cells expand, more colour appears, while the skin becomes lighter when they contract.

many harmless insects gain protection by mimicking the poisonous ones.

Colours for Display

This use of colour is shown best in birds and they, of course, have fairly good colour vision. The male of the species is usually more brightly coloured than the female and uses his brightly coloured feathers to attract a mate. An outstanding example of this is in the peacock which erects his huge tail feathers to attract the hen. Colours also trigger off other reactions such as feeding. Some young birds open their beaks to be fed when they see the shape or colour of the parent's head.

The disruptive pattern of the left-hand snake distracts from the whole shape which would be more obvious were the snake of a single colour (right).

CHAPTER TWENTY-FOUR

Animals that Change Colour

IF a dark coloured chameleon is put on a leafy branch, it will seem to disappear from sight in about fifteen minutes. It is one of a number of animals that gain protection by changing their colours to blend in with the background. The colour change is a physiological process involving redistribution of pigments in the skin.

Most of the animals that can change their colours have the pigments in special colour cells called *chromatophores*. Insect pigments, however, are scattered in ordinary cells. Chromatophores – of which the best known are the *melanophores* containing black pigment – respond to light and, in a lesser degree, to temperature. Although in some animals, the actual colour cells expand and contract, it is more common for the pigment to be withdrawn into the centre of the cell or spread out along the branches.

There are two distinct types of colour cell response. One, known as direct or primary response, is caused by light falling on the cells themselves. Strong light causes the pigment to expand and the overall colour of the animal becomes darker. The pigment contracts in dim light and the animal becomes pale.

The other type of response – indirect or secondary – is via the eyes and

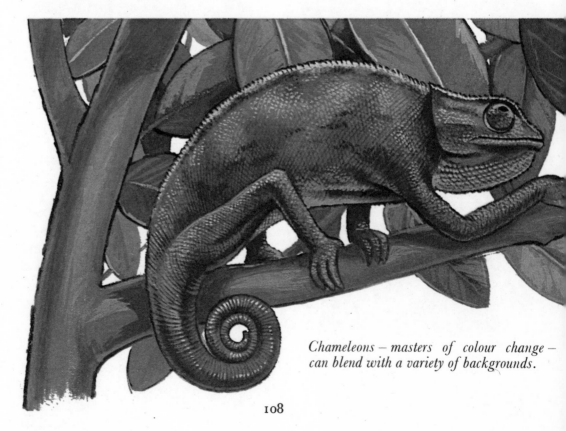

Chameleons – masters of colour change – can blend with a variety of backgrounds.

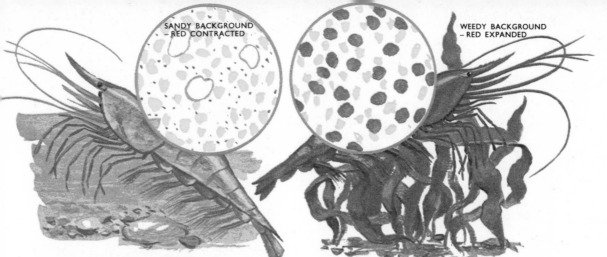

Prawns from sandy and weedy pools. The colour change is brought about by hormones acting on the red, white and yellow colour cells.

the brain. When the eyes detect a dark background, messages arrive at the colour cells causing them to expand and produce a darker coloration. A light background similarly produces a contraction of the pigments. The primary and secondary responses, therefore, do not always act in the same direction.

The messages to the colour cells may be in the form of direct nerve impulses from the brain. Alternatively, the brain may cause the release of hormones that act on the colour cells. In many animals, both nerve and hormone messages are concerned with the control of the colour cells.

Colour Change in Invertebrate Animals

In all invertebrates other than squids and their relatives, colour change is brought about by hormones. Prawns in a sandy pool blend so well with the sand that only an occasional movement betrays their presence. Their coloration is controlled by numerous colour cells scattered all over the body surface. Small cells containing yellow pigment are widely scattered. Others, containing red pigment, are found especially around the tail. Larger colour cells with both red and yellow pigment occur in bands and patches. Other large colour cells contain opaque white and red pigment.

A prawn in a sandy pool has its yellow and white pigment expanded, giving it a mottled appearance to match the sand. The red pigment is contracted into tiny dots. Prawns from a weedy pool are darker – the red pig-

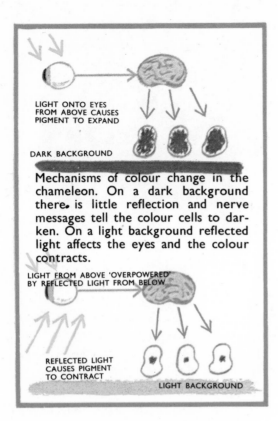

LIGHT ONTO EYES FROM ABOVE CAUSES PIGMENT TO EXPAND

DARK BACKGROUND

Mechanisms of colour change in the chameleon. On a dark background there is little reflection and nerve messages tell the colour cells to darken. On a light background reflected light affects the eyes and the colour contracts.

LIGHT FROM ABOVE 'OVERPOWERED' BY REFLECTED LIGHT FROM BELOW

REFLECTED LIGHT CAUSES PIGMENT TO CONTRACT

LIGHT BACKGROUND

A flat-fish can resemble some artificial backgrounds. The colour cells are controlled by nerves but the cells themselves do not change size. The pigment moves within them. Expanded pigment produces darker overall colour, just as large black dots on a newspaper produce dark areas and small black dots, lighter areas.

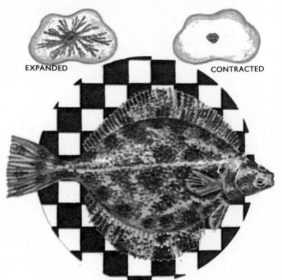

EXPANDED   CONTRACTED

ment is expanded and the white contracted. If these dark prawns are put on a sandy background a startling change occurs. The red pigment withdraws into dots, the yellow contracts a little and the white expands. In an hour or two the change is more or less complete but perfect adjustment requires a day or so. The reverse change occurs equally well. This colour change is mainly indirect, depending on the signals received by the eyes. There is, however, an important direct response of the colour cells. If the prawns are put on a sandy background in full light, they will never become completely adapted because the light causes the red pigment to expand a little.

Colour Change in Vertebrate Animals

Both nervous and hormonal control of colour exists in bony fishes. Nerve impulses are normally responsible for quick changes in response to a changing background but hormones are often concerned in the final colour adjustments.

Flat fishes (e.g. Plaice) are well-known for their colour-changing ability. They contain black pigment together with others ranging from yellow to red. Combinations of these are enough to produce a likeness to the majority of natural backgrounds. Flat-fish can even produce a reasonable copy of a chess-board pattern if the colours are available in its skin. Such detailed control of colour is possible only with nervous control. Hormone control, because the hormone passes round the body in the blood, can produce only over-all colour changes.

Amphibians, such as the frog, can

BLACK EXPANDED

RED EXPANDED

YELLOW EXPANDED

RED AND YELLOW EXPANDED

The cuttlefish (*Sepia*) and its relatives, the squids and octopuses, show the most rapid colour changes in the animal kingdom. The pigments – black, red and yellow – are enclosed in tiny colour cells in the skin. The black pigment cells are on the inside and the yellow on the outside. Each colour cell has its own muscles which, when stimulated, cause the cell itself to expand or contract. The muscles are activated by nerve impulses direct from the brain. This is a far quicker method than the secretion of hormones.

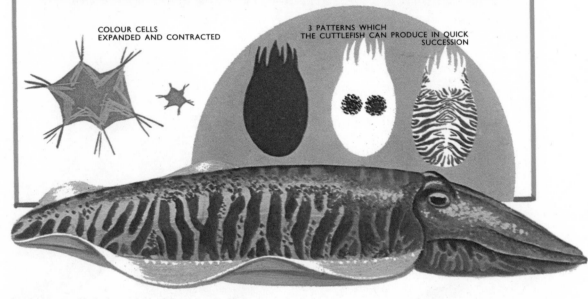

COLOUR CELLS EXPANDED AND CONTRACTED

3 PATTERNS WHICH THE CUTTLEFISH CAN PRODUCE IN QUICK SUCCESSION

darken or lighten the skin according to the background. This is a hormonal control mechanism. Some lizards show only hormonal control of colour but others, including the chameleon, appear to possess only nervous control. The chameleon skin has several layers – a brown or black one at the base, followed by white and blue layers (produced by optical effects) and a layer of yellow pigment cells. The combination of any of these layers can produce colours ranging from yellow, through greens and bluish greens, to brown and black. Each colour cell is connected to a nerve and colour change may be very rapid. In the dark,

chameleons are rather pale-coloured but in dim light, they become darker. The eyes are stimulated by light and messages are sent to darken the skin. Strong light can act on special receptors in the skin and a reflex action causes darkening. Reflected light from a light-coloured background stimulates the eyes in a different way and causes the colour cells to contract and produce a pale colour. In bright light, however, this action does not completely overcome the darkening reaction to light and the animal does not become completely pale. There is still much to be learned about the details of colour change in the chameleon.

CHAPTER TWENTY-FIVE

Imitation in Nature

THERE are probably over one-and-a-half million different kinds of living animal. Many of these kinds number thousands of millions of individuals. It is, therefore, hardly surprising that there is a great deal of competition among animals; there is truly a 'struggle for existence'. This great competition has led to every conceivable form of defence and attack. Speed, armour plating, warning coloration and foul smell are often used as survival means. Some of the most interesting and remarkable adaptations, however, are those concerning camouflage and mimicry.

Camouflage involves the resemblance of the animal to its surroundings so that it is inconspicuous to its predators and, indeed, to its prey. Some of the best examples are to be found among the insects. Many butterflies, although they may be brightly coloured on the upper side, resemble leaves when at rest. Stick-insects and

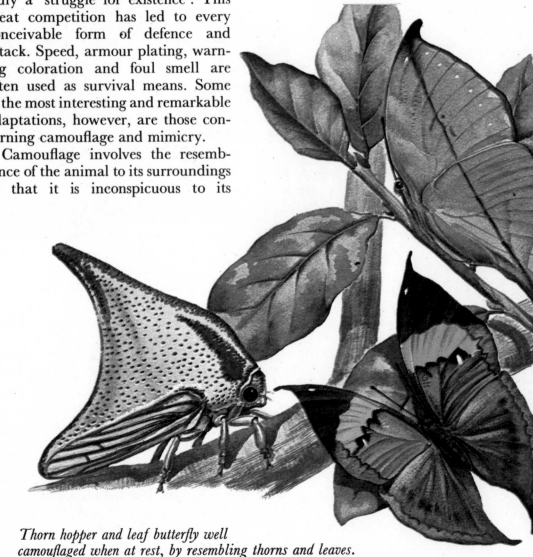

Thorn hopper and leaf butterfly well camouflaged when at rest, by resembling thorns and leaves.

leaf-insects are other well-known examples. Several species of tree-hopper are almost indistinguishable from thorns when sitting on the appropriate twigs and various cater-pillars resemble twigs themselves. Some sea-horses are disguised so well that they completely disappear against a background of sea-weed.

It must not be thought that the animals concerned copy their surroundings in order to merge with them. This is very bad zoology. The resemblances must have been there to start with and the *Theory of Natural Selection* can be used to explain the close similarities. Individual animals vary a lot and some would have resembled the surroundings more than others. The better camouflaged ones thus stood more chance of surviving and their offspring too, resembled the surroundings. Gradually the present form was obtained for all the individuals.

Mimicry is the name given to the cases where an animal derives benefit from resembling another animal rather than its surroundings. It is just a special case of protective coloration and can be explained by the Theory of Natural Selection. Among so many species of insect it is not unreasonable to assume that a number of them will look alike, and if one species is protected – by evil smell, sting or warning colours – other similar-looking ones will also derive benefit. The resemblance will then be continued and improved by natural selection over many generations.

In 1861 a naturalist named H. W. Bates was travelling along the Amazon and observed that large numbers of black and brown butterflies were congregating despite the presence of many insect-eating birds and other animals. The butterflies were protected by having a distasteful flavour but occasionally there appeared specimens of a very different kind. They looked like the common ones but lacked the distasteful flavour. Bates realised that the edible species were protected from enemies by virtue of their resemblance to the other butterflies and that here was an example of mimicry. This type of example, where a harmless species imitates a harmful one, is known as *Batesian* mimicry.

The animals that are 'copied' are

These two butterflies are both distasteful to birds and benefit by sharing a similar colour pattern. This is Mullerian mimicry.

Bees and wasps are mimicked by many insects. The Drone fly is a true fly but, when feeding from flowers, it looks very much like a bee.

DRONE FLY   HONEY BEE

called the *models* and the others, the *mimics*. Predators soon learn that certain types of insect or certain colour patterns are associated with stings or vile taste and they leave

A good Batesian mimic is the harmless Bee Hawk (bottom) which greatly resembles a bumblebee when in flight.

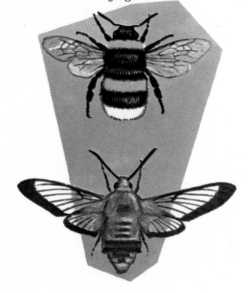

all such insects alone. The mimic thus gains protection. Even if only one per cent of the mimics are saved, there is a great advantage. The model and mimic must obviously live in the same areas and mix freely. They must also behave in a similar fashion. For example, many spiders mimic ants. The spiders have dark marks on their sides that give the appearance of a narrow thorax while the front legs are held out rigidly in front as if they were antennae. All this would be useless if it were not accompanied by the correct behaviour, and so they dash to and fro in the urgent manner of ants, mingling with them so well that even trained entomologists have captured them thinking they were ants.

Obviously, for this type of mimicry to be effective, the models must be much commoner than the mimics. If this were not so, the predators would be quite likely to associate good food with the colour pattern and both

SPIDER

The behaviour of the spider and the way that it holds its front legs out in the manner of feelers, allow it to mingle safely with ants.

An assassin bug (bottom) that mimics a small wasp on which it feeds.

mimic and model would decline.

There are, however, many instances, notably among tropical insects, in which both models and mimics are common, and both are distasteful to predators. This type of mimicry is called *Müllerian*, after the Brazilian naturalist Müller who described it in 1879. There may be two or more similar species. The advantage of the system is seen in the training of would-be predators. Suppose a bird requires 150 attempts before it realises that certain insects can sting. If a second species is also distasteful, three hundred insects will die before one bird learns to avoid these two species. However, if the two insect species share a common colour pattern, only seventy-five of each will perish. Thus the mimicry is effective and the more species sharing the pattern the better.

So far, the examples considered have all been those of animals avoiding capture, i.e., for defence. The same mimicry can also be used to disguise attack. The saying about wolves in sheep's clothing is quite true in nature. We have, therefore, a third type of mimicry – that in which a predator imitates its prey so that it can have the element of surprise in its favour. The most remarkable examples of this type of mimicry are to be found amongst the Assassin-bugs, a very apt name. These are carnivorous creatures and live upon various other insects. They are remarkably like their prey, even to the smallest detail so that some species resemble stick insects while others look like mosquitoes or even, in one case, the Praying Mantis. The Assassin bugs can deceive even human collectors.

CHAPTER TWENTY-SIX

Nocturnal Life

NIGHT comes and a great change-over takes place in the animal world. The creatures of the day seek their resting places. An entirely new population wakes and emerges. Man retires indoors at twilight and turns on the electric light. Usually he remains unaware of the shifting pattern of life outside.

The night creatures spend their active lives in very poor illumination. When the sun has set the only light comes from the stars or from what sunlight is reflected by the moon or the sky. In response to this limitation, eyes have become specialized to react to the minimum quantity of light. Other sense organs – notably smell, hearing and touch – have become acute.

But night may be beneficial. It is cooler and consequently the humidity or dampness of the air is increased. Many invertebrate (backboneless) creatures have little or no protection against drying up during the day and so they emerge only after sunset. Examples are earthworms, slugs, snails, and woodlice. In deserts where water is always scarce nearly all animals appear only during the cooler more humid night. The intense heat of the day is avoided by burrowing beneath the ground.

Vision at Night

The light sensory tissue of the eye – the retina – is found at the back of the eye-ball. Light rays are concentrated on to its surface by a lens. The cells which make the retina are of two

kinds – the rods and cones. Cones are the least sensitive to light and come into use only when illumination is good. In Man, and a few other mammals they are also responsible for colour vision. The rods are much more sensitive to light. They are the cells

THE LONG EARED BAT USES ITS MOUTH TO EMIT VIBRATIONS (A VESPERTILIONID BAT)

THE LESSER HORSE-SHOE BAT EMITS VIBRATIONS THROUGH THE NOSE (ARHINOLOPHID BAT)

Bats navigate in the night by emitting bursts of ultrasonic vibrations. The vibrations are reflected by obstacles and the echoes picked up by the sensitive ears, inform the bat the distance and nature of the obstacle. One group of bats emit the initial vibrations through the mouth. The other group fly emitting vibrations through their noses.

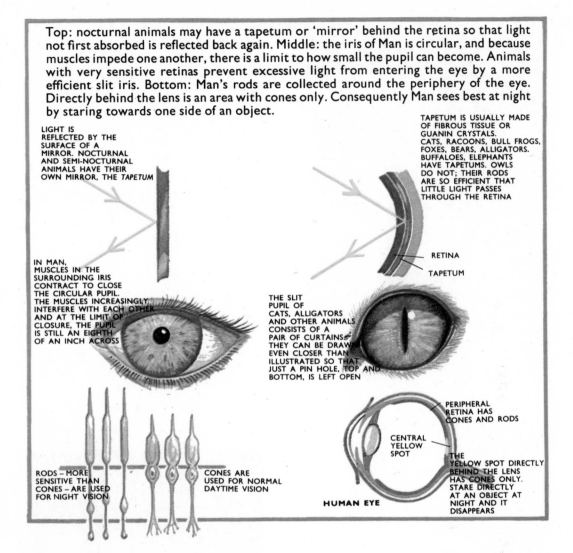

Top: nocturnal animals may have a tapetum or 'mirror' behind the retina so that light not first absorbed is reflected back again. Middle: the iris of Man is circular, and because muscles impede one another, there is a limit to how small the pupil can become. Animals with very sensitive retinas prevent excessive light from entering the eye by a more efficient slit iris. Bottom: Man's rods are collected around the periphery of the eye. Directly behind the lens is an area with cones only. Consequently Man sees best at night by staring towards one side of an object.

LIGHT IS REFLECTED BY THE SURFACE OF A MIRROR. NOCTURNAL AND SEMI-NOCTURNAL ANIMALS HAVE THEIR OWN MIRROR, THE *TAPETUM*

TAPETUM IS USUALLY MADE OF FIBROUS TISSUE OR GUANIN CRYSTALS. CATS, RACOONS, BULL FROGS, FOXES, BEARS, ALLIGATORS. BUFFALOES, ELEPHANTS HAVE TAPETUMS. OWLS DO NOT; THEIR RODS ARE SO EFFICIENT THAT LITTLE LIGHT PASSES THROUGH THE RETINA

RETINA

TAPETUM

IN MAN, MUSCLES IN THE SURROUNDING IRIS CONTRACT TO CLOSE THE CIRCULAR PUPIL. THE MUSCLES INCREASINGLY INTERFERE WITH EACH OTHER AND AT THE LIMIT OF CLOSURE, THE PUPIL IS STILL AN EIGHTH OF AN INCH ACROSS

THE SLIT PUPIL OF CATS, ALLIGATORS AND OTHER ANIMALS CONSISTS OF A PAIR OF CURTAINS. THEY CAN BE DRAWN EVEN CLOSER THAN ILLUSTRATED SO THAT JUST A PIN HOLE, TOP AND BOTTOM, IS LEFT OPEN

PERIPHERAL RETINA HAS CONES AND RODS

CENTRAL YELLOW SPOT

THE YELLOW SPOT DIRECTLY BEHIND THE LENS HAS CONES ONLY. STARE DIRECTLY AT AN OBJECT AT NIGHT AND IT DISAPPEARS

RODS – MORE SENSITIVE THAN CONES – ARE USED FOR NIGHT VISION

CONES ARE USED FOR NORMAL DAYTIME VISION

HUMAN EYE

used at night when illumination is poor. They cannot however detect colour.

Man's eyes possess both rods and cones – approximately a million cones and 100 million rods. He is able to see not only in daylight but also in poorly illuminated places or at night. Night vision is only in silvers and greys for it is the rods that are providing visual information and they lack the ability to discriminate colour. More specialized night creatures possess only a few cones in their eyes and some bats have none at all.

Another property which makes Man's eyes good for seeing at night is the diameter of the eye-ball. It is about 1 inch across – a fairly large structure. The larger the eye-ball the greater the quantity of light that can be received. Cats, foxes, and other night creatures, have large eye-balls. The owl's eye-balls are in fact so expanded that they cannot swivel in their sockets, instead this night hunter has to move its whole head from side to side if it wants to see in a different direction. Horses, bears, lions, deer and buffaloes have large eyes and

The soft-feathered, silent flying owl is a true nocturnal animal; it rarely makes sorties during daytime. The retina of the eye is highly sensitive, hearing is acute. Also, the owl is one of the few birds with *binocular* vision. The eyes are well-forward, side-by-side so that an object is viewed by both of them together. This means there is double the chance of detecting a victim.

Many animals – particularly the larger ones may be active during day or night, they have adequate sense organs to manoeuvre in the dark; bear, deer, skunk, lion, horse, pig, even Man himself.

For shy, browsing herbivores night is safer than day. In the dark, enemies – even well adapted ones – can be more easily avoided. For the same reason, animals whose numbers have been reduced by hunting or disease tend to become nocturnal until numbers are restored. The rabbit is an outstanding example.

are animals with good day and night vision.

A spectacular adaptation to the night vision of some hunting creatures is an internal mirror (*tapetum*) at the back of the eye. If any of the light passing through the retina fails to be absorbed, it can be reflected by the mirror back through the retina. Everyone has noticed how a cat's eyes glitter in the light of a torch. The glitter is really the torch light reflected back through the pupil by the mirror.

Other Senses

Sensitivity to light is just one method by which an animal can learn about its surroundings. Other sense organs also convey information and at night when illumination is poor they are of particular value. Some night creatures in fact have little use for their eyes at all.

The hairs of mammals and the feathers of birds not only provide

insulating layers against the cold. Each structure is provided with a tiny nerve fibre; if the hair comes into contact with some object, immediately the animal is aware of the interference. The hairs are *tactile* or sensitive to touch.

Particularly sensitive are the large bristles or *vibrissae* extending from the sides of the animal's face. Night creatures whether they have good night vision or not have very well developed vibrissae and also have extended hairs from their eyebrows. Passing through dark holes and tunnels the bristles touch the sides and tell the creatures the dimensions of the space. If the bristles touch another animal, then they trigger off a violent reflex action. A cat will snap out its paw in anticipation of its victim, a mouse will flee for its life.

Certain feathers covering the faces of nocturnal birds are similarly

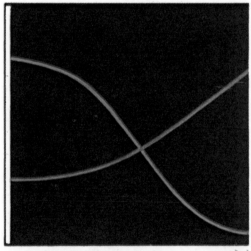

As temperature falls so humidity rises. The moist atmosphere brings out many creatures which during the heat of the day would be in danger of drying up. The high humidity also facilitates the sense of smell.

specialized. The owl is well equipped with them and so is the night-jar.

The sense of smell is also independent of light and the humid atmosphere at night is very suitable for the carrying of odours. Small creatures such as field mice and shrews are particularly reliant upon their noses for information; their eye-balls are correspondingly small and inefficient for night vision. They search for berries and insects largely by scent and touch. Moths about at night are attracted to flowers partially by odour; the scent is detected by the sensitive antennae.

Hearing is the other important sensation and it may be acute in night animals. Each animal however may communicate with its fellows by sound without giving itself away. Different creatures have their own channel of sound waves. The vibrations of the air they make with their tongues and mouths are only detectable by carefully attuned ear drums of their own species. The night – though silent to **Man – may be filled with noises that he cannot perceive.**

Bats are remarkable for using their own sounds as a navigating device. The noises are produced by the tongue and escape through the nose or a corner of the mouth at very high frequency. The sounds bounce back from surrounding objects, and these echoes are detected by the bat's trumpet-like ears. The rapidity and strength of the return provides a detailed account of the obstacles in the bat's path. The bat is almost seeing with its ears. It does have eyes, but its true sight does not have to be good. This echo-location enables it to fly through a forest at darkest night, locating and capturing insects as it passes.

Countering the bat's radar, some moths are covered in fuzzy scale which deadens the echo. Alternatively they are able to detect the high-pitched sounds of the bat's cry, and drop to the ground.

Bats, though by far the best echo-locaters, are not unique in their powers. Field mice and shrews have also been shown to navigate in the dark using the echoes of their own sounds as a guide. Man, too, with experience can make use of the phenomena; blind persons can often find their way without bumping into obstacles by listening to the echo of their footsteps or the tap of their stick.

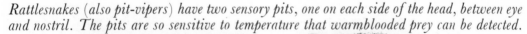

Rattlesnakes (also pit-vipers) have two sensory pits, one on each side of the head, between eye and nostril. The pits are so sensitive to temperature that warmblooded prey can be detected.

CHAPTER TWENTY-SEVEN

Keeping Afloat

FOR an object to float, its density must be no greater than the water in which it is floating. In other words, its weight must be equal to, or less than, the weight of an equal volume of the water.

Some organisms in the sea solve the problem of keeping afloat in just this manner. Their overall density is less than sea water. Amongst the plankton – plants and animals drifting in the surface layers of the sea – some microscopic plants (*diatoms*) owe their low density to oil globules filling vesicles inside them. Some small protozoan animals are partially filled with water made less dense by saturation with carbon dioxide or ammonia gas.

Alternatively, to keep afloat a shape may be developed which has a very large surface area in comparison with the animal's total volume. The larger the surface area in contact with the water, the greater the frictional resistance to sinking. Small plants and animals living in the plankton may be flattened, ribbon-shaped or drawn out into long slender pencil shapes. Spines – projections from the surface of the organism – may be developed, both in plants and animals. As a rule, organisms in tropical seas are far more spinose than those in colder, denser waters. A bigger surface area is required to prevent sinking. Some organisms are actually able to modify the length of their spines according to the viscosity of the water. A third mechanism for keeping afloat is, of course, by swimming.

Variations on a Theme

Creating buoyancy by a lowering of density is found throughout the animal kingdom. But variations are found both in techniques and structures used.

Some of the most highly evolved of the jellyfish family (the *coelenterates*), despite their large size and overall weight, have solved the problem by the development of air sacs. Air sacs increase the volume of the body without contributing much to an increase

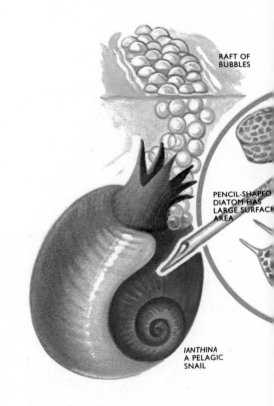

RAFT OF BUBBLES

PENCIL-SHAPED DIATOM HAS LARGE SURFACE AREA

IANTHINA A PELAGIC SNAIL

in weight. The result is a lowering of density. Perhaps the best known is *Physalia* – the 'Portuguese man-of-war' which has an enormous bulbous air sac (*pneumatophore*) – probably developed from a fold of skin. The sac floats above the surface of the waves and supports the rest of the animal. A similar device is used by the Sargasso seaweed which keeps afloat using air-filled bladders. *Ianthina*, a planktonic snail, actually makes its own bubble raft. Gas is secreted and contained in thin films of mucus.

For animals which, in their search for food, move from one level to another, the ability to both rise and sink without spending energy in swimming is a great advantage. Such an ability requires a method of controlling the animal's density – that is, its weight relative to its volume.

Some fish possess a swim bladder – a balloon-like sac positioned above the gut. Gas is secreted into the bladder from the blood system. The weight of the heavy bony skeleton and muscle tissues which cause the fish to sink is off-set by the lightness of the inflated bladder. The result is that the fish can float without expending energy – a freedom which no doubt has been a great evolutionary advantage. At lower depths, however, the pressure of the water increases, the gas inside the bladder is compressed. The volume of the fish is lowered, its density is increased. Counteracting this effect, more gas is absorbed by the bladder from the

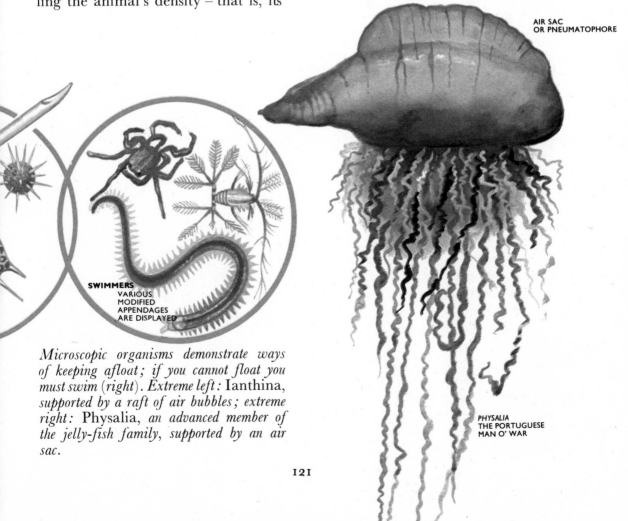

AIR SAC
OR PNEUMATOPHORE

SWIMMERS
VARIOUS
MODIFIED
APPENDAGES
ARE DISPLAYED

PHYSALIA
THE PORTUGUESE
MAN O' WAR

Microscopic organisms demonstrate ways of keeping afloat; if you cannot float you must swim (right). Extreme left: Ianthina, *supported by a raft of air bubbles; extreme right:* Physalia, *an advanced member of the jelly-fish family, supported by an air sac.*

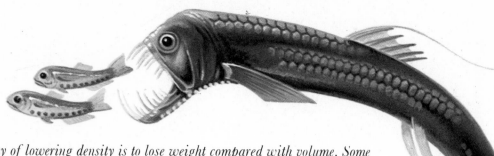

One way of lowering density is to lose weight compared with volume. Some deep-sea fishes have their bones and swimming muscles and the rear parts of their skeletons so reduced that they can hardly swim. The front parts of the body are not affected and the fish lie in wait for prey.

blood, so keeping the sac at a constant volume. The gas pressure may rise inside the sac to an enormous degree. For instance, fish swimming at 15,000 feet need a pressure of 7,000 pounds per square inch inside the bladder to withstand the sea's pressure.

Not all fish have swim-bladders. The sharks and their allies (the cartilaginous fish) have never had lungs and consequently have never developed swim-bladders. They constantly swim in order to keep up, and are not nearly so stable. Some degree of buoyancy is, however, obtained from special oils in the liver.

Of the bony fish, bottom-livers such as the plaice have lost their swim-bladders altogether. So have some fast-swimming bony fish – the mackerel and the tunny. The reason underlines one of the drawbacks of the swim-bladder as a hydrostatic organ. In changing its volume according to the depth of the sea, some length of time is required. Secretion and absorption of air is a delicate operation. Thus if a fish caught in a trawl net is brought rapidly to the surface, the bladder will burst, causing damage to the other internal organs. Consequently mackerel and tunny, though they must swim to keep afloat, nevertheless may move rapidly from one level of the ocean to another.

The volume of a solid is not so influenced by high pressures as gases, and in some fish a strong development of fatty tissues is found around the lung. But fat has a density of 0.9 – only slightly less than water, and consequently must be present in fairly large quantities to be effective.

One other mechanism of lowering density is to dispense with as much as possible of heavy tissues. Thus some bottom-dwelling ocean fish have a much reduced skeleton in the tail region. The swimming muscles are poorly developed and appear delicate, almost transparent. The proportion of dilute body fluids and fatty tissues is increased and the body density is just less than water.

Among the invertebrate marine creatures the cephalopods – a group of molluscs – are the most highly evolved. They live in shallow waters about the coast as well as in the deeps.

A very spectacular cephalopod is *Nautilus* – the last survivor of a stock that goes back 500 million years. The colourful spiral shell in which it lives is divided into chambers. The outside chamber is the largest and it is here that the animal is situated. The other chambers have become gas-filled. A strip of tissue extends back through the chambers and appears responsible for the gas secretion. It is this development of a buoyancy mechanism in early cephalopods that probably first

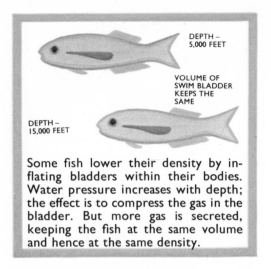

Some fish lower their density by inflating bladders within their bodies. Water pressure increases with depth; the effect is to compress the gas in the bladder. But more gas is secreted, keeping the fish at the same volume and hence at the same density.

enabled them to develop an active swimming mode of life rather than a bottom-living habit.

Most numerous of the cephalopods today are the cuttle-fish. Along the back of this creature is the chalky internal shell – the well-known cuttlebone. The cuttlebone, when examined in detail, is found to be a beautiful structure consisting of layer upon layer of calcite plates neatly joined by calcite columns.

The rigidity of the cuttlebone gives the cuttlefish support as it swims through the water. But also the bone

The cuttlebone of cuttlefish not only gives support. Spaces within the 'bone' (inset) can be filled either with air or water so changing the creature's density.

gives buoyancy for, being largely hollow, its density is 0·6. The cuttlebone is not just a static organ, its density can change. When the cuttlefish wishes to sink, the chambers in the cuttlebone are flooded with water. When rising, the water must be pumped out again – a process which appears to be carried out by osmosis.

Yet another variation is found in some deep water squids – allies of the cuttlefishes. These squids have solid chitinous internal shells which, though acting as a skeleton, have no hydrostatic function. Nor is there any kind of air-filled bladder present, or much fatty tissue.

Early Nautiloids probably secreted air into the chambers of their shells just as Nautilus *does today.*

The riddle of the squid's floating ability – for it can float at all levels – rests in its body fluid. The body fluid occupies two-thirds the weight of the squid but has a density of about 1·01 compared with sea water's 1·02. The density of the fluid is low because of ammonium ions present in solution – ammonia being the nitrogenous waste.

123

CHAPTER TWENTY-EIGHT

Regeneration

EACH species of plant or animal has a characteristic form that distinguishes it from other species. The typical form is reached by complicated development from the fertilized egg. When, by some accident, part of the structure is damaged or lost, the organism strives to regain its original form This ability to grow replacement parts is called *regeneration*. In general, the rate of regrowth is proportional to the amount of regrowth required to reach the original form. All animals and plants are capable of it to some extent but, as a general rule, the more highly evolved an animal is, the less are its powers of regeneration. Man, for example, is able to regenerate skin and bone tissue to mend wounds and fractures, but is unable to regrow even a finger if one should be lost. Some internal organs can be regenerated if a large enough part remains as a starting point. The liver is an example; so, too, are the adrenal glands. The replacement of worn-out tissues is a form of regeneration and goes on throughout life. The most obvious is the replacement of skin from below as the outer layers rub off.

Some animals are able to regenerate new limbs – in fact lizards may actually shed their tails themselves to confuse enemies and later they grow new ones. Crabs, too, can throw off a limb to escape from an enemy. The most striking cases of regeneration, however, are found among the lower animals – the Coelenterates (jellyfish and their relatives) and the flatworms.

Flatworms are built up of three basic layers: an external *ectoderm*, an *endoderm* lining the gut, and a *mesoderm* occupying the space between the two. Planarians are flatworms with great powers of regeneration. As long as all three types of tissue are present, a complete new worm can grow from a tiny portion.

When a planarian is cut in half, both halves can form new animals. The cells of the damaged region lose their individuality and all become alike. They grow and divide and the growing mass takes on the correct shape – be it of a head or a tail. Gradually the cells become specialized again and begin their normal functions. The head region is the coordinating region and, if missing, is always the first formed structure in a regenerating body. Not until there is a head, can the other organs be reformed.

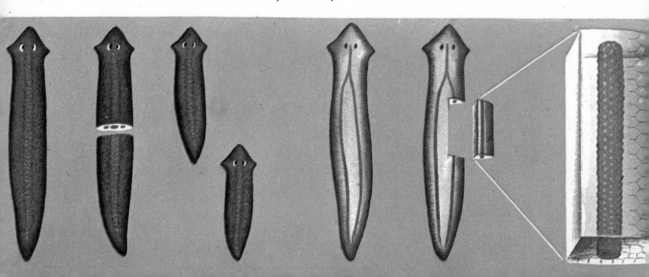

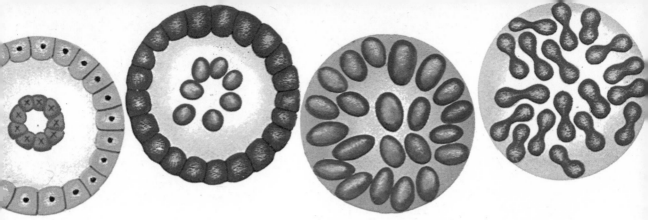

he damaged tissue is ade up of specialised in and gut cells.

These specialised cells become unspecialised, gut and skin cells become alike.

The cells of the unspecialised tissue then start to grow.

The number of unspecialised cells increases as they divide.

A fragment of a flatworm can regenerate into a new individual as long as there is sufficient food reserve in the tissue. The fragment has no mouth and feeding organs and so cannot get any food from outside. The cells at the cut surface (sometimes all the cells in the fragment) become alike and multiply. Because food is used up during this process, the fragment gets smaller, but if sufficient cells can be formed, a tiny planarian will develop. Any original organs remaining in the fragment will be partly absorbed so that they conform in size to the rest of the new animal. A new head is formed before the rest of the body develops.

Any fragment of a planarian that regenerates naturally will produce a head at the original front end. Although the cells are completely reorganised they never lose this *polarity*. Regeneration in jellyfish is very similar, but in higher animals, the head cannot be regenerated. New limbs and bodies can form under the influence of the head but not vice-versa.

Earthworms are able to regenerate new bodies as long as the front part containing the vital organs is present. The tail region of a worm, if removed, cannot continue its existence. Crabs, lobsters and crayfish are able to break off their limbs at will – a process called *autotomy*. More important, they are able to regenerate the lost parts. At the base of each limb is a special muscle which bends it until it breaks at a specially weakened place, the *breaking point*. At first only a miniature replacement limb is formed, but when the animal next sheds its skin the limb grows rapidly to almost the size of the original limb.

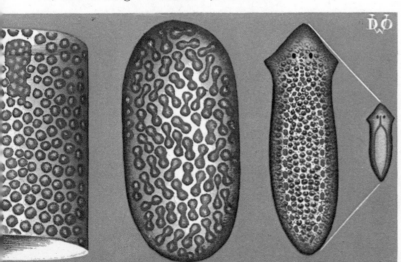

If a flatworm is cut in half each piece will regrow. The front quickly grows a tail, but the tail has to form a head before forming the missing organs. A whole new flatworm can regenerate from a tiny portion, providing skin and gut cells are present. The enlarged drawings show what happens to the flatworm fragment as it is reorganised to form a tiny flatworm the size of the fragment. Gut and skin cells become unspecialised. These then divide and eventually take on special tasks again when they are sorted into their correct positions to form a new flatworm.

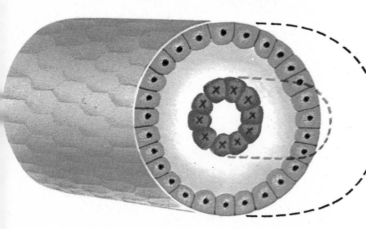

The growing mass of unspecialised cells is gradually reorganised in the exact pattern of the original part in shape, size and proportion. The new skin and new gut cells having taken up their proper positions, they begin to work at their specialised jobs, and the regenerated part begins to function as a normal active part of the flatworm.

Insects, too, possess the power of regeneration, when young. Missing legs and antennae (feelers) can be regenerated but do not develop fully until after at least one moult. A pad of regeneration tissue develops at the wound and forms the missing limb. Many abnormalities of regeneration are known among insects – a mantis has, for example, been known to grow a leg where an antenna had been lost.

One frequently sees starfishes with one or more arms missing. The mouth and part of the digestive organs are in the central disc of the animal and thus it can continue to feed even when all the arms are lost. Its powers of regeneration are such that the starfish can develop new arms from the central disc alone.

Regeneration in vertebrate animals is much more limited. Lizards can regenerate lost tails but rarely is the new one full sized. Newts have been known to regenerate limbs and tails, so too have young frogs. In the higher animals, the powers of regeneration are confined to the mending of broken bones and connective tissues and the regrowth of some damaged internal organs.

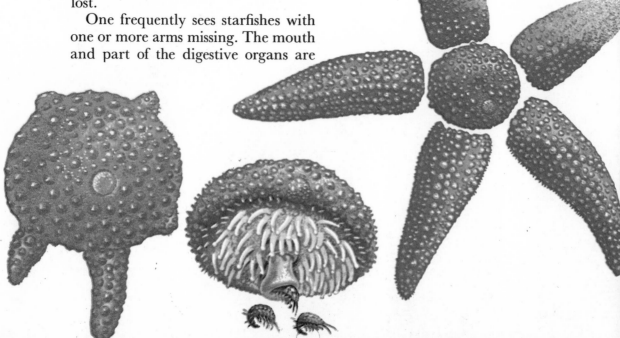

Index

128